SENSE RELAXATION

Below your mind

by bernard gunther
photos: paul fusco
design: william hopkins

Collier Books, New York

Library of Congress Catalog Card Number: 68-24112

Second Printing 1968

First published in a hardcover edition by
The Macmillan Company.

The Macmillan Company, New York
Collier-Macmillan Canada Ltd., Toronto, Ontario

Printed in the United States of America

For information on
Sensory Awakening records write:
Sensory Awakening
Esalen Institute
Big Sur, California 93920

for my
mother
father
teachers

Ida Rolf
Oscar Janiger
Frederick Perls
Charlotte Selver
Jacques Hondorus
Richard Hittleman

much very many special thanks to: sue macy jim wade rae herley dick price mike murphy paul herbert june schwartz george leonard john bleibtreu my students and the people of esalen

what is
LIFE ALL ABOUT

JOY   mystery   experience   feeling   awareness   alive   LOVE

NOT:

excessive-words-anxiety-tension-
   deadness

to continually be
tense
is DIS/ease

TENSION does not come
from outside you
it is something that you produce.
Excessive TENSION
is a non-verbal message
from your body
asking you
to become more receptive
permissive, to let go
and relax.

RELAX

NOW
Listen

after reading
the following instructions
take your time
and carry them out.

Sit straight, not rigid
in a chair.
Close your eyes
and follow your thoughts
for 1 minute.
Then let the words go and
become aware of how you feel,
not how you think you feel
or how you'd like to feel
but your actual feelings
and sensations as they are
in the next minute.
Now shift your attention
to your feet and
without moving them in any way
become conscious of what they
are resting on.
Then take 15-20 seconds
to feel-experience
(rather than think or imagine)
the following areas
of your body:
your feet, each of your toes
(without moving them),
the top of your feet, your ankles,
calves, knees, thighs,
buttocks, the chair
that is supporting you;

your stomach, chest, back,
the back of the chair;
your shoulders, arms, elbows,
forearms, wrists, hands,
each of the fingers;
your neck, lips, cheeks,
nose, eyes, face;
forehead, top of the head,
back of your head:
your entire body.
Experience your breathing,
the sounds in the room
and how you feel right now
and then slowly open your eyes.

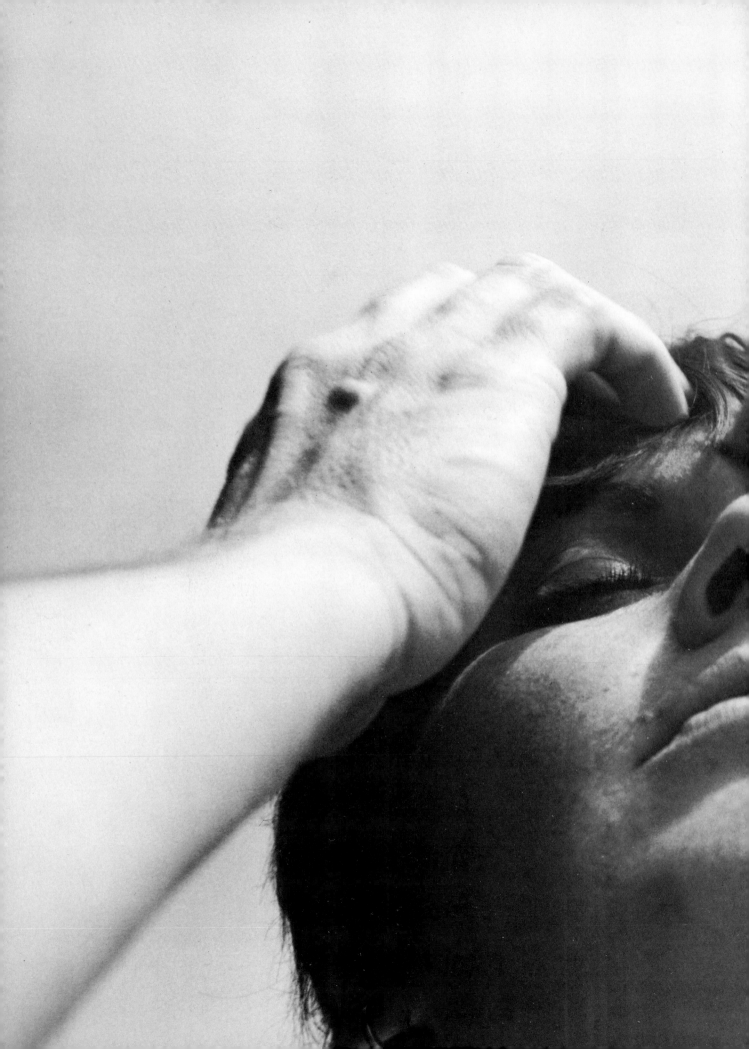

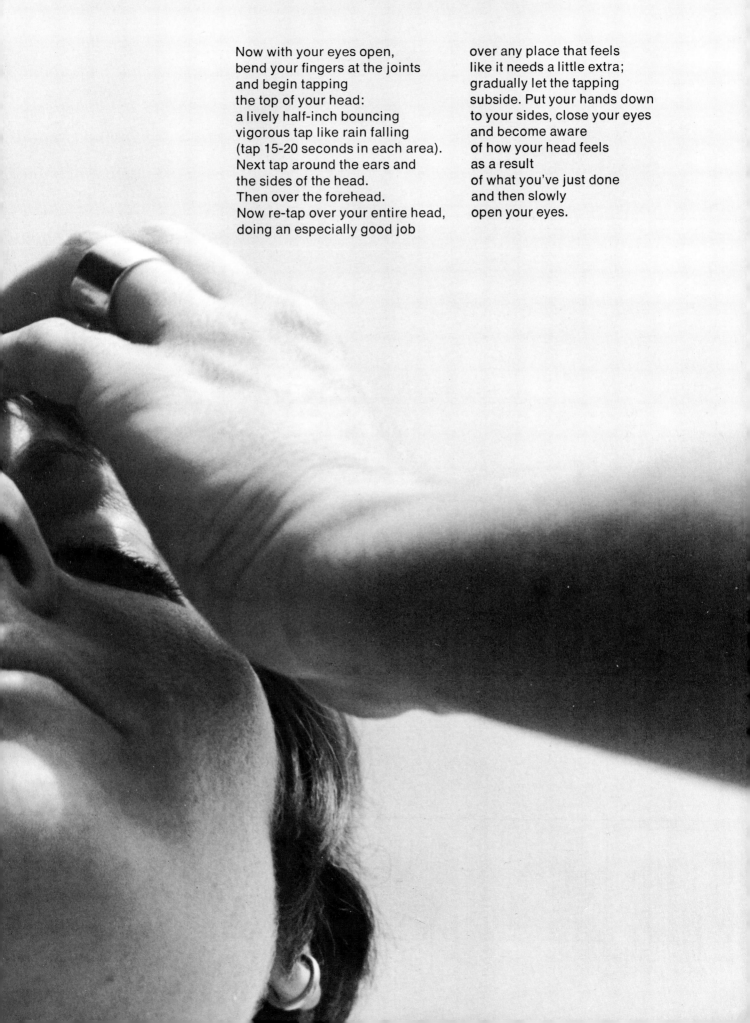

Now with your eyes open,
bend your fingers at the joints
and begin tapping
the top of your head:
a lively half-inch bouncing
vigorous tap like rain falling
(tap 15-20 seconds in each area).
Next tap around the ears and
the sides of the head.
Then over the forehead.
Now re-tap over your entire head,
doing an especially good job

over any place that feels
like it needs a little extra;
gradually let the tapping
subside. Put your hands down
to your sides, close your eyes
and become aware
of how your head feels
as a result
of what you've just done
and then slowly
open your eyes.

Now close your eyes
and slowly
bring your hands
towards your face;
the heels of your hands
come to rest on the cheeks,
the palms cover the eyes,
the fingers rest
over the forehead.

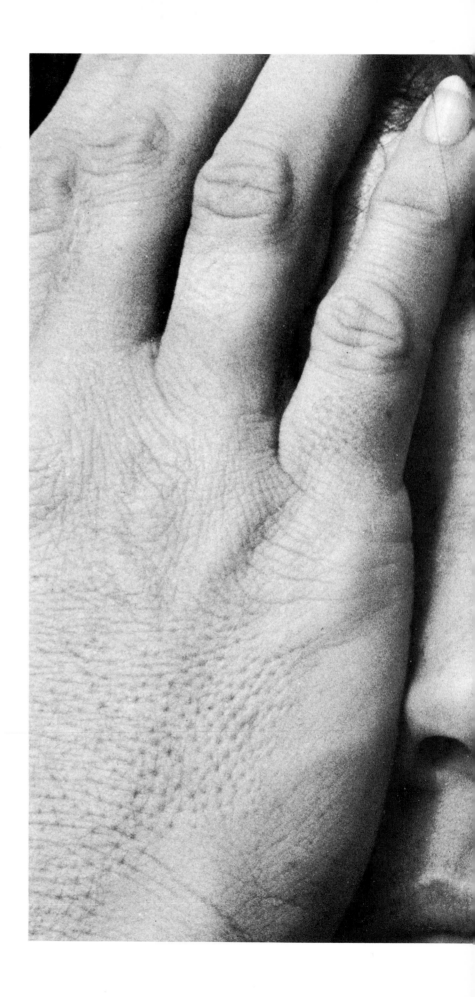

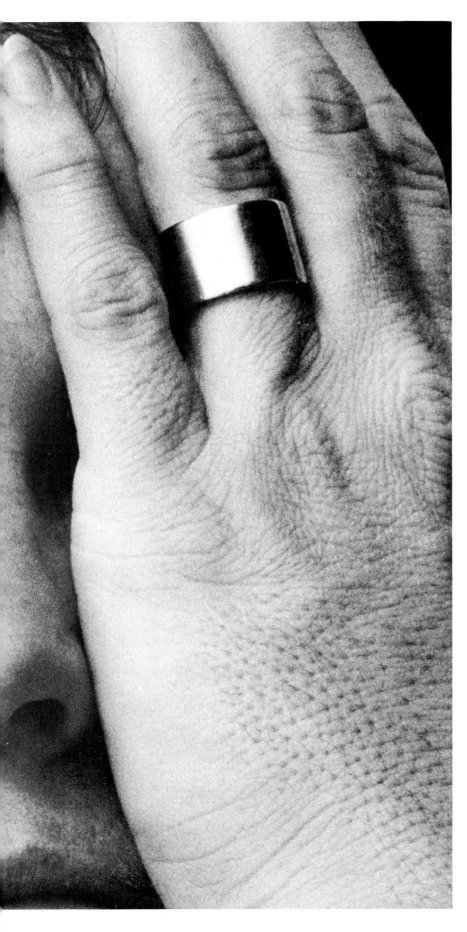

Stay with your eyes covered
for 1 minute;
be sensitive to your eyes
and the inside of your head;
feel how things are there;
without creating any changes,
just allow
whatever wants to occur.
Slowly take your hands away,
experience how you feel
and open your eyes.

The practical part
of this non-book
consists of games to do
to aid you to un/do
to re/do. The
experience-experiments will
allow you to feel
more sensitive, aware
of tension; letting go,
feel free: help
your self.

you know it all already:
but
you have forgotten:

REMEMBER

Chapter 1
SENSE

Children by nature
are sensitive,
involved in sense play
and exploration:
in-a-sense.
Social and formal education
stress the cognitive
and motor functions
of the organism
without regard
for sensory development.
We teach them non-sense.
This lack of sensitivity creates
desensitization:
an imbalance in being;
a loss of feeling;
senseless: inhibition-alienation-
depression-anxiety-deadness.

Experiments:
sensory deprivation,
a total cutting off
of sense contact, causes
hallucinations, disassociation
and total disorientation.

We are organisms
composed of organs.

The eyes-ears-nose-mouth-skin:
the five sense organs.
Babies are biologically organized,
whole: seeing, hearing,
smelling, tasting, touch-feeling
directly without preference.
We condition them to specialize:
eye dominance.
I dominate my organism: seeing
is believing,
see for yourself,
great men are seers
and visionaries:
when we leave someone, we say
"see you later,"
never touch, or taste or
smell you later.

See what I mean?

The problem
with eye specialization
is that it tends to separate
(especially when accompanied
by excessive thought and
chronic tension).
Seeing can divide space,
keep things at a distance: I
(separate from the world)
see differences.
What would happen
to the racial question
if we were all blind?

20

In our ignorance
of the other senses,
we become imbalanced, tense,
insensitive.
Listening to content
rather than tone, rhythm,
or pitch,
we lose contact with
the subtle messages of nature
(all around) un/sound.
Eating canned-frozen-
artificially flavored food:
is that why we have developed
such bad taste?
Just look at most of our art,
architecture, movies.
Smell has become a bad word
and whole industries are
devoted expressly to its
elimination. But
the greatest avoid/dance
concerns the largest organ
of the body: the skin.

Young monkeys
deprived of touch
and closeness
suffer from a lack of
relatedness;
even their physical growth
is stunted.

A lack
of physical contact
in children
leads to heightened irritability
depression and
in extreme cases, autism:
the loss
of the will to live.

At a certain point,
we stop touching children;
we teach them to keep their hands
to themselves,
to not even explore themselves.
They-we learn-teach
to stay away from one another;
to keep our distance;
conditioning at arm's length;
shake hands quickly
and avoid real contact. Sex
is the only chance we
really have to touch each other
and it is often confined
to so-called erogenous zones.
Is it any wonder that we are
tense, anxious, alienated;
out of touch with our total body;
that we are dis/integrated,
dis/organized?
That we need to rebalance,
to re/integrate, to re/organize?

Sensory Awakening
is a method
which can help
bring you back to your senses:
to quiet excessive thought,
to release chronic tension,
to enhance direct sensory-reality
in the here and now.
This process
can show you how to allow
greater sensitivity,
feeling and awareness: aid you
in letting yourself
be more—
your entire organism—open
to the potentialities
and possibilities
with out/in you.

Chapter 2
SELF AWARENESS

zen's answer
to socrates

no thyself

Here are revitalizers:
energizers, tranquilizers,
which will allow you
to release–relax–refresh–
without the use of drugs.
Take as needed—
fill your own prescription.

General Instructions

1) Wear comfortable,
loose fitting clothes.
Ladies will prefer:
shorts, slacks, or leotards.
2) All times given are
aproximate and subject to
feeling and circumstance.
3) Keep talk
to an absolute minimum
during and immediately after
each experience.
4) Doing the preludes to
each experiment is desirable
but not always necessary.
5) Experiments
marked (e) are energizers,
those marked (t)
are tranquilizers. They may be
mixed and used
according to individual
needs.

There is no right or wrong
in these experiments:
they are experiences and
not exercises.
Exercises are done automatically,
repetitiously with some goal
in mind. The activiites in this
part of the book
have the no goal of feeling,
allowing, being your
body.

There is no correct response
to these experiences
except that which
your body expresses. The point
is not to judge but
to be aware.

Introduction to Tapping and Slapping Yourself

Tapping and slapping stimulates nerves, increases blood flow, opens every area of the body to being more alive.

Suggestions for self slapping:

1) Allow your hands to take the shape of the area being slapped, your wrists are loose.
2) It is a vigorous, gentle slap that slightly stings, but does not hurt.
3) Don't be heavy handed. Don't beat yourself up.
4) Continue to breathe during the slapping. Don't hold your breath.
5) When using both hands slap simultaneously.

Suggestions for self tapping:

1) Bend your fingers at the joints.
2) Tap with an up and down bounce-like motion, raising and lowering fingers approximately one-half inch.
3) Use both hands simultaneously.
4) Don't be too hard or too light. The tap will usually have a slight tingling effect over the area being worked on.

Suggestions for self touching:

1) Stay alive in your entire hand (palm and heel as well as the fingers).
2) Touch firmly but gently.
3) Allow your hands to take the contour of the area being touched.
4) If it is a still motionless touch, once you make contact your hands stay where they are and do not move around.
5) Moving touches vary in types and degrees from a caress to a firm-gentle squeeze.
6) Let your feelings tell you how long to stay and when to move away.

25

Tapping

Head Tapping (e)

Close your eyes
and experience how your head
feels.
Open your eyes,
bend your fingers at the joints
and begin tapping
the top of your head.
Use a lilting motion
like rainfall
all over your head
(an even vigorous tap).
Tap around 15-20 seconds
in each area.
Allow the fingertips to bounce
one-half inch as you tap.
Tap the whole area
of the back of your head.
Then tap all around the ears
and the sides of the head.
Now tap over the forehead.
Re-do any area
that seems to be asking for more.
Tap gently over the whole area
of the head
and then gradually
let the movement subside;
stop. Put your hands down,
close your eyes,
and experience the after effects
of this tapping.

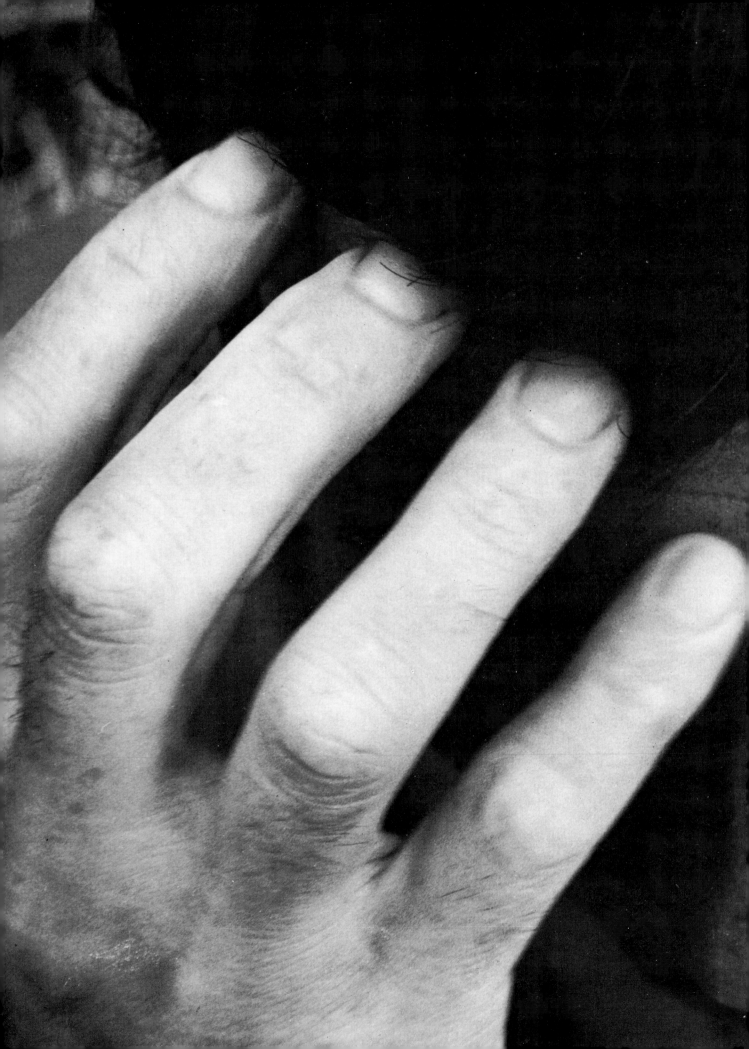

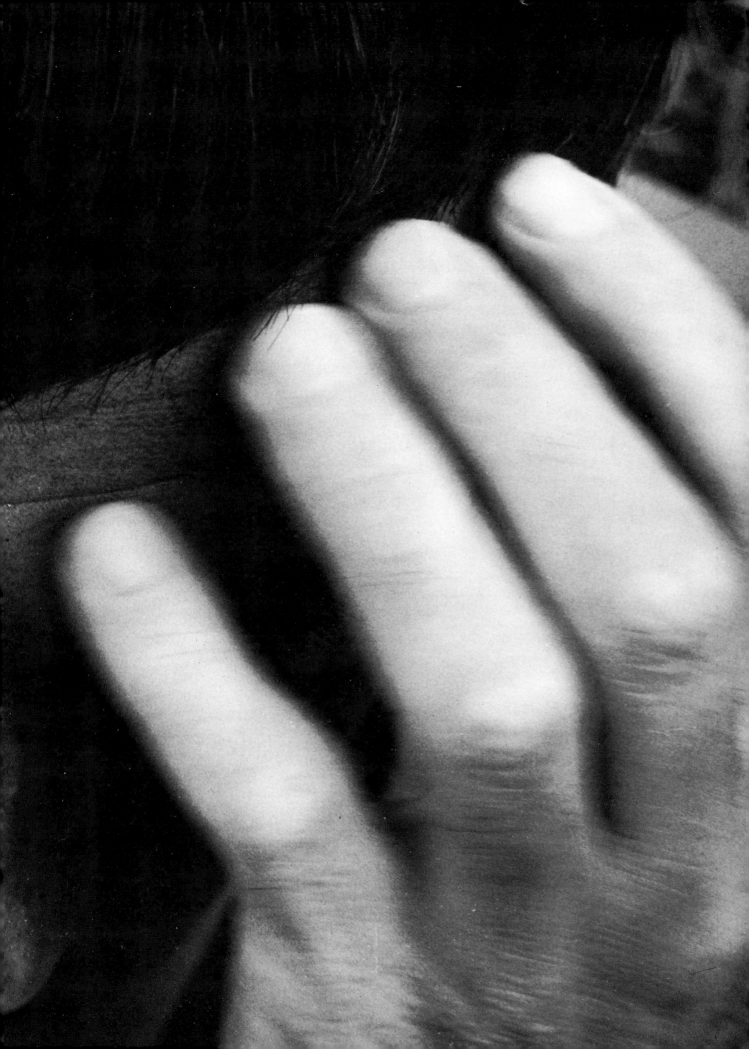

Slapping

Head Slapping (e)

Prelude: Head Tapping.
With your eyes open
slap the top of your head with
the flat of your hand-fingers.
Slap vigorously, but gently.
(Spend 15-20 seconds in each
area.)
Use a bouncing motion;
hands move about one-half inch.
Now slap the back of your head.
Move down to the back of
your neck. Slap without jarring.
Now slap over the sidehead
and over the forehead.
Repeat slap in any area
that feels like it wants more.
Slap gently the whole area.

Slowly and gradually
let the slapping subside.
Put your hands down,
close your eyes
and experience the result
of this slapping.

Face Slapping (e)

Close your eyes
and experience your face.
As your eyes remain closed
begin slapping your forehead
with your fingers.
(Slap 15 seconds in each area.)
The hands are held semi-flat
and meet the face simultaneously
so that there is no jarring.
Now to the jaw.
Slap vigorously there,
using palms as well as fingers.
Next over the cheeks
with your fingers. Then
the lips and chin.
Go gently over the nose.
Use just the

fingertips over the eyelids.
Then go over any part
that seems to ask for more.
Gently slap over the entire
face again. Stop,
lower your hands and
experience the results.

Slapping

Arm Slapping (e)

Shut your eyes.
Become aware of your arms.
Experience how they feel. Now,
with your eyes open,
extend your left arm
in front of you at shoulder level.
With your right hand
slap both the top and bottom
sides of your left arm
from shoulder to fingertips.
Use an even, vigorous slap.
Go 3-4 times up and down
both sides of your arm. Then
gently over the whole area again.
Next, bend your left elbow
so that it is at right angles
with your left shoulder. Now,
shake your arm for 15 seconds;
be loose in your wrist and elbow;
allow your left hand to wave
back and forth freely.
Slowly and gradually let your arm
come down to your side.
Close your eyes and experience
the arm you have worked on.
Contrast it with the opposite
arm. Open your eyes and
do the other arm.

Chest Slapping-Yelling (e)

Prelude: Chest Slapping.
With the palms and fingers
of your hand held flat, slap
the entire area of your chest.
The motion is vigorous
but in no way painful.
As you continue slapping,
move back above the breasts
and make the sound "Ahhhhhh"
(the sound you're asked to make
by the doctor
when he depresses your tongue).
The sound is continuous and
as loud as possible.
Yell-slap for 15-20 seconds.
Gradually let the yelling and
slapping subside.
Put your hands down.
Experience the after effects.

Most people are half breathers,
keeping residual air
in their lower lungs;
they are unable to take a full
deep breath even if they want to.
To breathe deeper
you must exhale more. Yelling
gets out all the old air and
some of those held-in feelings;
let yourself be open-air.

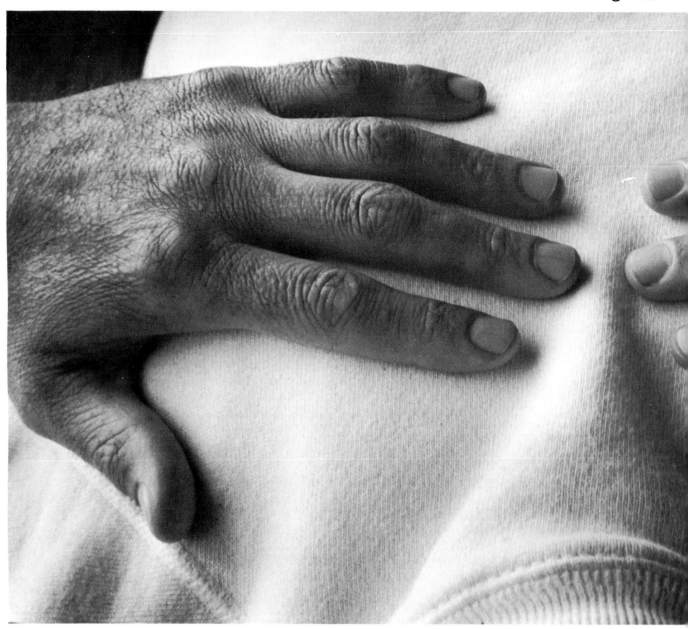

Breathing in Touch (t)

Prelude: Chest Slapping.
Lie down on the floor
and close your eyes. Take
a few moments to experience
your body and its relationship
to the floor. Now,
become aware of your breathing.
Make no effort to change it;
just watch and allow.
After 30 seconds, place
both hands on your upper chest,
above the breasts, so that
the palms are flat

and the fingers of one hand
do not overlap or touch
the other. Experience the space
between your chest
and your back.
After 30-60 seconds, slowly
place your hands at your sides.
Take a few moments to feel
the results of this touch. Next,
place your hands on your
solar plexus, the area
just above the navel
and become aware of what if any
movement you find there.
Again, after 30-60 seconds,

put your hands down at your sides
and be with your feelings.
Finally, place your hands
on your lower belly, just inside
of your frontal hip bones,
just above the pubis.
As your hands rest there,
shift your attention to your
nostrils and experience
the air as it moves in and out.
After 30-60 seconds
bring your hands to your sides
and, again, become aware
of how you feel.

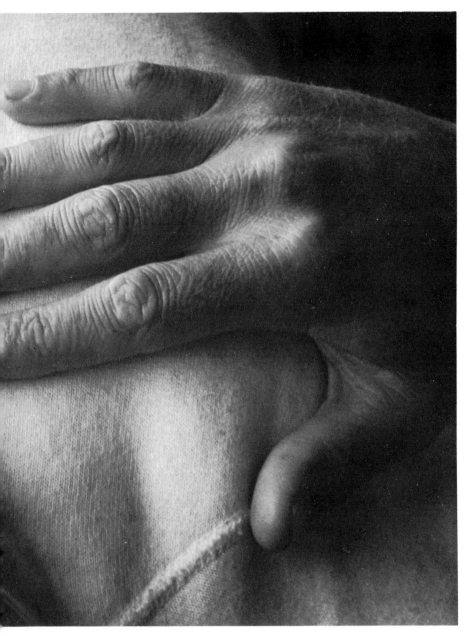

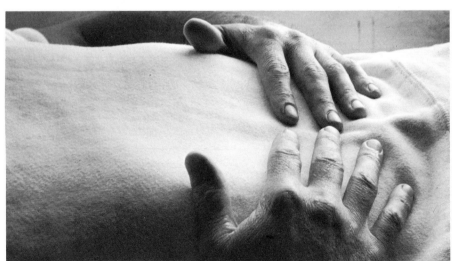

Shaking

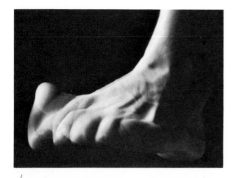

Shake a Leg (e)

Prelude: Leg Slapping.
Supporting yourself on your
right leg, wiggle your left toes.
(Spend 10-15 seconds in this
and each of the following areas.)
Move this dance
into your left foot, extending
and contracting the foot.
Explore all of the movement
possibilities in your left ankle.
Next, move around in your calf.
Let the motion carry into
your knee and thigh, twisting
and turning in every way.
Eventually include the hip.
Now shake your entire left leg,
causing it to vibrate vigorously
from hip to toe.
Slowly let the shaking subside.
Put your leg back down
on the floor. Close your eyes
and experience your left leg.
Do the other leg.

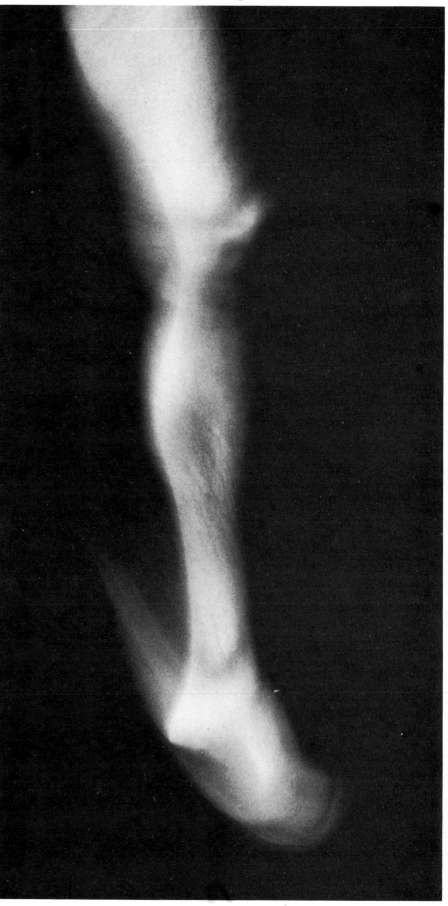

38

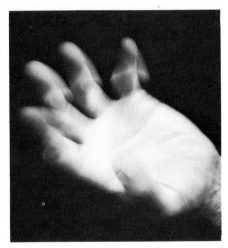

Shake an Arm (e)

Prelude: Arm Slapping.
Do a dance, wiggling the fingers
of your left hand.
(Spend 10-15 seconds in this
and each of the following areas.)
Next, bring this dance
into your left hand, making and
extending your fist.
Then, explore the movement
possibilities in your left wrist,
twisting in all directions.
Now, move around
in your forearm.
Extend the movement into
your elbow. Next, let the motion
carry into your upper arm,
twisting and turning every way.
Then include the shoulder
and all the range of movement
possible there. Finally,
raise your arm so that it is
even with your shoulder and
vigorously shake the entire arm.
Slowly let the shaking subside.
Your arm comes down;

close your eyes and experience
how your arm feels. Contrast it
with the other arm. Follow the
same procedure on the other arm.

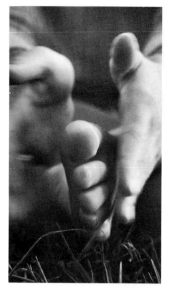
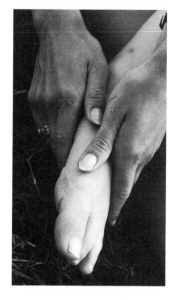
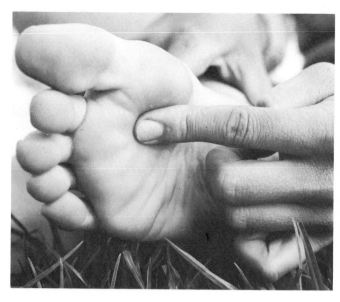
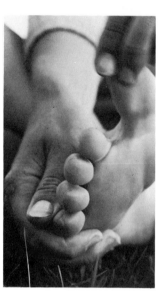
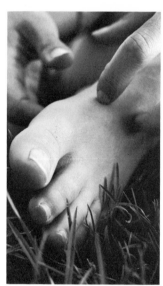
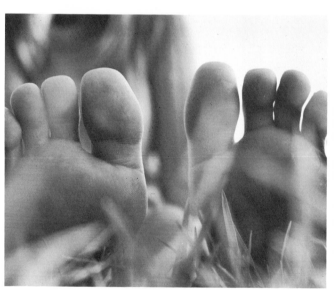

Foot Slapping (e)

Sit Down. Place your left ankle
on top of your right thigh.
Slap the bottom and top of your
left foot with both hands.
It is a gentle vigorous slap.
Then, slap the sides of the foot.
Next with one hand do the bottom
of the foot. Now both hands
over the entire foot.
Gradually let the slapping
subside. Put your foot down.
Close your eyes and
experience how your foot feels.
Do the other foot.

Foot Noting (t)

Prelude: Foot Slapping.
Sit down and
put your left ankle on top
of your right thigh.
With both hands feel the top,
side and bottom of your foot.
With a fingertip press in
on the bottom of your foot.
Become aware of its softness.
Gently pinch-poke
the entire bottom of your foot.
Then pull out and wiggle
each toe individually.
Scratch your foot; caress it.
Close your eyes
and with your hands explore
your entire foot.

Now, stretch your leg out and
experience how your foot feels.
Stand up on both feet
and feel the difference between
your two feet.
Open your eyes and experience
how walking is. Then
do the other foot.

40

Slapping

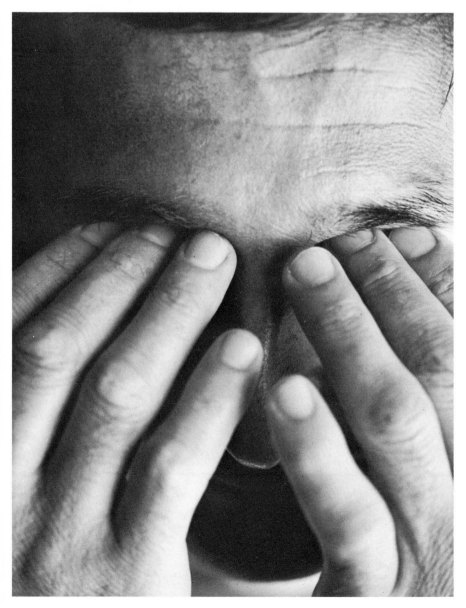

Palming (t)

Prelude: Face Slapping.
Lie on your back with your hands
down at your sides.
Close your eyes
and experience how they feel.
Now, slowly bring your hands up
toward your face,
until the palms of your hands
rest over your eyes.
The heels of your hands
rest on your cheeks,
your fingers lie over your
forehead. Hands remain still
in this position for 30 seconds.
Now, slowly take your hands away
and place them at your sides.
Experience the results
of this first touch.
Then slowly bring your hands
towards your eyes again.
This time the heels of your hands
rest on your eye sockets. <u>Do not</u>
<u>press</u> against the eyeballs.
The palms of your hands
rest on your forehead; fingers
over your hairline.
Remain this way for 30 seconds.
Slowly take your hands away
and experience the effects of
this touch. Allow 20-30 seconds
between each touch. Now, slowly
bring the tips of your index
and third fingers up until they
rest gently on your eyelids.
<u>Do not press</u>. Remain here for
30 seconds. Slowly,
take your hands away
and place them at your sides.
Experience how your eyes feel,
now open them
and look around you.

Lifting

Arm Lift Standing (t)

Prelude: Arm Slap-Shake.
Stand, close your eyes
and experience your arms.
After taking 20 seconds,
slowly spread your fingers apart
with an even, gentle pressure.
Keep your elbows straight
and this pressure in your hands
as you slowly-smoothly
raise both arms until they are
even with your shoulders.
Take at least 15-30 seconds
for the lift.
Allow your arms to remain
in this top position
for 10-15 seconds. Now, slowly
concentrating on your fingertips
and experiencing the movement,
lower both arms
back to your sides.
Take 15-20 seconds to feel
the results. Do the lift
2 or 3 times.

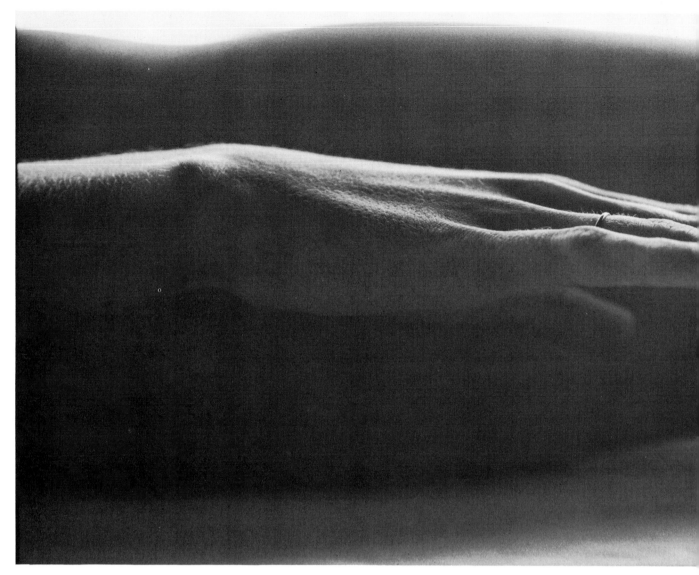

Lifting

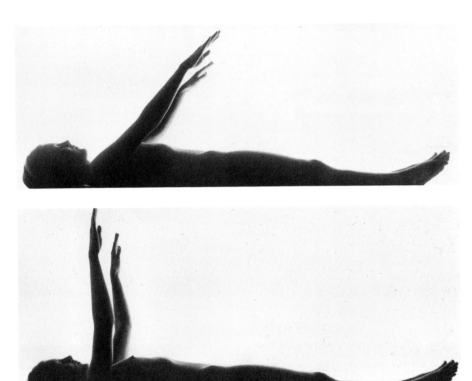

Arm Lift Lying (t)

Prelude: Arm Slap-Shake.
Lie on the floor
with your arms at your sides.
Close your eyes
and feel your arms.
After taking 30 seconds,
slowly spread your fingers
as wide as they will go.
Keep your fingers spread
and arms straight.
Slowly and smoothly raise them up
parallel to each other
until they are at right angles
with your shoulders.
Take at least 15-30 seconds.
Allow your arms to remain there
for 10-15 seconds.
Now slowly, concentrating
on your fingertips,
lower your arms to your sides,
taking at least 15-30 seconds.
Allow plenty of time
to experience the results.
Repeat the movement
two or three times.

Shoulder Lift (t)

Prelude: Shoulder Slapping.
Stand up, close your eyes
and experience your shoulders.
After taking 10-20 seconds,
hunch both shoulders
in slow motion
as high as you can.
Take at least 15-30 seconds.
The movement upward is not jerky,
but continuous. When you reach
the extreme position,
hold the shoulders there for
10 seconds. Then slowly
let them down,
taking 10-20 seconds
and experiencing each aspect
of the motion.
Allow your shoulders to settle
where it feels right
for them to be.
Take plenty of time
to experience the effects.
Repeat the movement
two or three times.

Lifting

Lifting

Hip Lift (t)

Prelude: Leg Lift-Back Slap.
Lie on your back
with your eyes closed.
Take at least 15-30 seconds
for all of the motions to follow.
Slowly bring your knees up
towards the ceiling,
your feet remaining on the floor.
Experience how your back feels.

Now as if your hips were being
pulled straight up by a string,
raise your hips and buttocks
off the floor. Ever so slowly,
raise your entire spine off the
floor as high as you can, <u>your
shoulders and shoulder blades
remain on the floor</u>. Hold this
position 5-10 seconds.
Gradually, one vertebra at a time
lower your back to the floor.

Experience letting go
to the floor. Take 30 seconds
to feel yourself and the
floor now. Repeat, this time
raising only the lower half
of your back off the floor.
Hold top position for 10 seconds.
Be aware of making contact
with the floor as you come down.
Then take 30 seconds
to feel yourself

and the floor. This time, barely
raise your hips and buttocks off
the floor, approximately 1 inch.
Hold there 5 seconds.
Take as long as you can to lower
back to the floor. Experience
how the floor feels now; how you
feel now. Slowly straighten
your right leg; your left leg.
Feel how the floor is.
Open your eyes and sit up.

Lifting

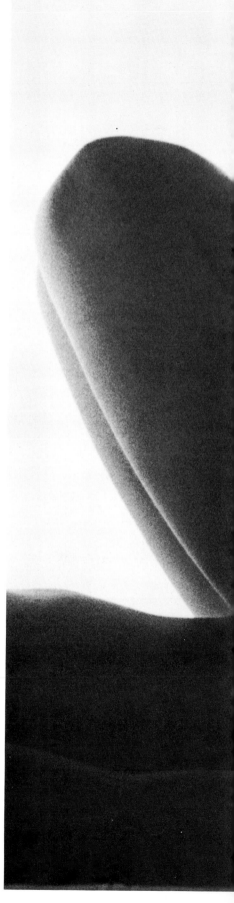

Leg Lift (t)

Prelude: Leg Slap-Shake.
Lie on the floor on your back.
Close your eyes.
Experience how you feel.
Take 15-30 seconds
for all of the motions to follow.
Slowly bend your left leg
so that your knee comes up
toward the ceiling while
your foot remains on the floor.
Do the same with your right leg.
Feel your back and its
relationship with the floor.
Slowly bring both knees in toward
your chest without raising your
spine off the floor. Gradually
lower both feet to the ground,
knees remaining bent.
Experience how you are now.
Slowly raise your left knee to

your chest, with your spine still
touching the floor.
Repeat with your right leg.
Gradually lower your left leg;
then your right leg.
Be aware of the moment
when your foot touches the floor
and what part of your foot
touches first.
After feeling the effects,
again raise both legs together
to your chest and
slowly lower them to the floor.
Experience how you feel now.
Slowly open your eyes.

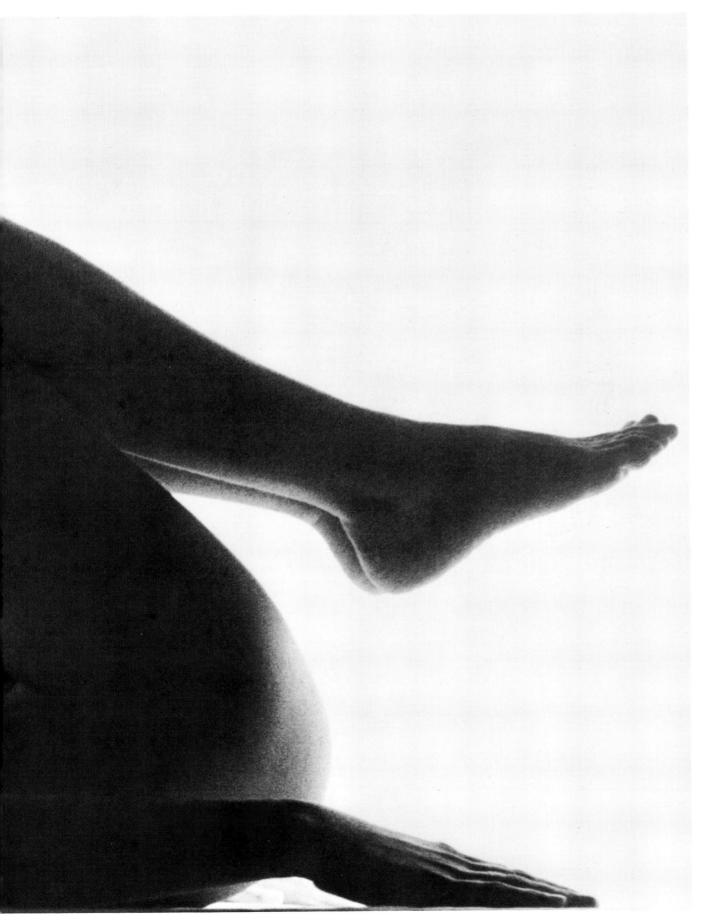

Stretching

Pillow Rock (t)

Prelude: Head Tap-Slap.
Materials: a round, flat rock,
3 to 5 inches in diameter. Sit
on the floor and close your eyes.
With your fingertips, massage
circles all over the back of your
head. Experience how
your head feels. Tap and pat
the back of your head.
Feel it now. Then lie down
on the floor on your back
so you are comfortable. Place
the rock under the back of your
head where it feels
most comfortable. Experience
the rock and its message,
asking you to open up and let go.
Stay with this experience
After a couple of minutes become
aware of how you feel. Remain
on your rock as long as you like.
Open your eyes.

The Lion (t)

Prelude: Face Slapping.
Lean slightly forward
with your shoulders. Allow your
eyes to widen as much
as possible. Open your mouth wide
and stick your tongue out
as far as you can. Don't
be inhibited. Be ferocious!
Tense and tighten
the neck muscles and cords
as well as those in the face.
Hold this position for
15-60 seconds.
As slowly as possible
allow your face and neck muscles
to return to normal.
Repeat 2-3 times.

Increases face circulation;
helps prevent/eliminate wrinkles.

Chapter 3
WORDS & TENSION

Children learn to avoid
feeling excitement
by holding their breath
or squeezing muscles.
Tightening against intense
pleasure-pain; emotions:
fear, anger, grief,
laughter, orgasm.
I being overwhelmed.
losing control . . . "you
must learn to control
your self."

Big boys don't cry
(if they tighten their diaphragms,
chests, and necks) . . . look
at the cowboy; the I-deal,
he has no fears, ain't got no
emotions, not even scar'd
of dyin', cause he's already
(dead pan). Most men
very early in their training
get Tom Mix-ed up.

Girls are sugar, spice,
everything nice and
just don't have sexual feelings
till you're married.
Keep your legs crossed
and freeze your pelvis (frigid).
Hold on—hold back
with hold.

Learn to conform:
to not express;
act like young ladies
and gentlemen, behave yourself
restrict your self
constrict your self.
You must try harder
make effort,
pay-a-tension.

Chronic
excessive muscular tension,
(Reich's character armor):
a system of habitual muscular
contractions that keep
a person's spontaneous impulses
in. A holding against
feeling, emotion, expression.
Repression, depression.
Depressing yourself.
Playing it safe;
under control; over control.

No longer serving
any productive function
this hold-on from childhood
absorbs energy; hinders
spontaneous body function:
sensation-sensitivity-creativity-
productivity-communication
and feeling.
Producing deadness, numbing
whole areas of the body;
inhibiting breathing, movement,
the flow of energy.
Fixation: stunting growth.
Creating in a person
the experience
of being blocked off,
in a dream-like state
of half-aliveness. Stuck:
separate from himself
and the world.

You can't trust your organism:
your self;
then how can you trust
your mistrust . . .
the double bind
of the body-mind.

"education is largely
verbal education"
(Aldous Huxley)

At home, in schools
we learn words: the fruit
of the tree of knowledge
of good and evil.
How to categorize and divide.
I become separate
from my body, from the world,
from experience. Roses are red
and the grass is green
and stress is placed on
similarities-differences,
rather than uniqueness.
Taught to forget about polarities
and relativity.
We must learn to filter alike,
be alike, to verbalize,
to analyze, to think what's real.

Most people think they feel
rather than feel.
Monitoring every experience:
label-limiting
the unique evolving differences
of each event. Talking
to themselves (euphemistically
called thinking); categorizing;
uninvolved distant.
Exchanging the excitement,
moment to moment
aliveness of direct experience
for dead
conceptualized existence.
Thing king.

Words ultimately become
hypnotic conditioning,
a series of expectations,
leaving little possibility
for the excitement of what might
be or really is.

This is not to condemn language
which when accompanied by
feeling
can be an extremely
exciting powerful delighting
creative communicative tool,
but only to recognize
the imbalance
that our society has produced.
Talking and thinking
have become compulsive
in many instances; a defense
against experience
and the world.

The problem of language:
nouns and verbs.
The actor
separate from the action.
I injured my finger
rather than just hurting.
Being the observer
rather than the experience.
There is no static aspect
of the self;
but thinking makes it seem so.
This hoax,
this commonly accepted fantasy
is a division
that starts the basic split;
within the mind ego
are all of the different aspects
of you: the good you,
the bad you,
the should you, the have you.
Endless talk, magic words
about reality
become realer than what is real,
until you are able to stop
and realize
you're only all
one self.

to know
is to
no know
so know
no know

To be is to be alive change
moving. Being human alive is
living on many different levels
of existence at the same time,
thoughts divide the mental
and the physical
which exist simultaneously.
Thinking, feeling, breathing,
seeing, circulation,
digestion happening
at the same time. They only seem
to be separate because
we think linearly, one thing
at a time; but
these events are not separate;

I am breathing
seeing
hearing
smelling
feeling
warm
excited
relaxed all at the same time

and really my experience
is none of these
which are only words, symbols,
which try to convey
my existence which is
every moment-alive-
change-moving-
NOW.

Excessive tension, words, sensory
limitation all lead
to automatic behavior.
Fixed conditioned behavior
based on rules, laws, concepts:
the way you should be:
self consciousness
does make robots of us all.
Automatic functioning is safe,
efficient, predictable.
Using tricks, techniques rather
than relating: manipulating.
Playing roles: maneuvers; control
controlling. Deliberate, phoney.
A lack of joy, honesty,
humor, love;
being bored to death.

Chapter 4
TWO DISCOVER

to know
experience
here and now
are some games
for two for you two
discover

Slapping Introduction

Like all everything else, there
are two sides to slapping;
most of us have been
over impressed by hurt-slapping.
Giving-slapping is
stimulating, encouraging,
elating: like a slap
on the back or
a pat on the head.

Suggestions for slapping others:

1) Allow your hand to be easy
(lots of give).
2) Let your hand take the
contour of the part of the body
being worked on.
3) Slap simultaneously
with both hands so as not to jar
your partner.
4) Allow your wrists
and shoulders to be easy.
5) Continue to breathe
while slapping;
if you hold your breath
you will tire very quickly.

Instructions for being slapped:

1) Keep your eyes closed
during the entire experience
unless instructed otherwise.
2) Allow your muscles-body
to be held easy, not stiff, so
that the effects
of the slap can move through you.
3) Don't try
to make anything happen or
keep anything from happening;
be open and aware.
4) Let your partner know
right away
if the slap is too hard
or if you would like
to be slapped harder.
5) Keep breathing;
holding your breath will hinder
the effects of the experience.

DO NOT TALK
DURING THE EXPERIMENTS
UNLESS INSTRUCTED

Follow instructions
even if they seem silly to you;
if you do them
they will make sense.

Suggestions for tapping others:

1) See and relate to
the area-person being tapped.
2) Be easy in your hands
and fingers; don't be over stiff.
3) Tap simultaneously
with both hands in an unhurried,
even rhythm.
4) After tapping specific places
go over the entire area
being tapped gently.
5) Continue to breathe
while tapping.

Instructions for being tapped:

1) Keep your eyes closed
during the entire experience
unless instructed otherwise.
2) Be easy in your body;
let the effects of the tapping
move through you.
3) Don't try to create anything;
allow what wants to take place.
4) Let your partner know
if the tapping is too easy,
too hard, or if you
wish him to continue longer.
5) Keep breathing:
before, after, during
let your breathing regulate
itself.

Instructions for touching others:

1) See-feel relate
to the person-area that is to be
touched.
2) Let your hands take the
contour of the area to be touched.
3) Touch slowly-gently, move
both in and away with sensitivity;
take at least 10 seconds.
4) Give your partner plenty
of time in between touches.
5) Don't move your hands or
fingers around once you
have established contact.
6) The touch is firm-light;
don't push down or squeeze your
partner.
7) Stay with what you're doing,
touching, rather than letting your
mind wander elsewhere.

Suggestions for being touched:

1) Keep your eyes closed
during the entire experience
unless instructed otherwise.
2) Be open in your organism and
let the effects of the touch move
through you.
3) Allow whatever wants to
happen.
Don't make anything happen or
keep anything from happening.
4) Let your partner know if
he is not touching right.
5) Keep breathing.

Tapping

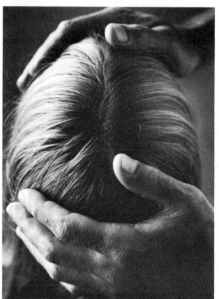

Head Tapping

Stand behind your partner.
The partner in front
closes his eyes. Bend
your fingers at the joints.
Begin tapping
the top of your partner's head.
The tapping is fast and bouncy,
not too hard, not too soft,
simultaneously with both hands.
The bounce is about
one-half inch off the head.
Allow 15 seconds for each area.
Tap all over
the back of his head,
around the ears, the side
of the head.

Now tap his forehead.
Go over the whole area gently-
quickly.
Slowly, let the tapping subside.
Move away.
Allow 30-45 seconds for
your partner to feel the effects.
Come around and
look at your partner's face.
Change places with your partner.

Head Touching

Prelude: Head Tapping-Slapping.
Place hands gently over the front
and back of the head. Front hand
goes over the forehead,
back hand directly opposite on
the back of the head.
Both hands always touch and
leave simultaneously.
Take care to slowly move away.
Each touch lasts about 45 seconds
with 30 seconds between touches.
Now place both hands
gently over the sides of the head
above the ears. Do not move
or apply extra pressure.
Leave without rushing away.

Touching

Next place hands gently
over the front and back of the
head. Front hand covers the
eyebrows with the lower palm
touching the bridge of the nose.
Back hand covers the lower half
of the back of the head and
the upper half of the back
of the neck.
Move away sensitively-slowly
and allow your partner to feel
the effects. Change places.

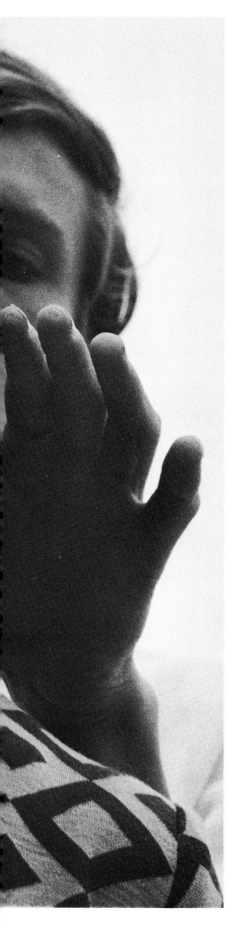

Shoulder Slapping

Stand in back of your partner and
take a look at his shoulders,
while he closes his eyes.
Allow 30 seconds
for him to settle.
Slap the entire area from the
beginning of the shoulders
at the edge of the neck
clear down to the fingertips.
There is lots of vitality
in the slap,
how vigorously depends on
the musculature of your partner.
Be gentle
over the back of the wrists
and hands which can sting.
Slap the area of the hands
and arms three times.
Move up and
do an especially good job
over the shoulders.
Then go over the shoulder blades.
Pat gently over
the entire area and move away.
Give your partner
30 seconds to feel the effects.

Touching

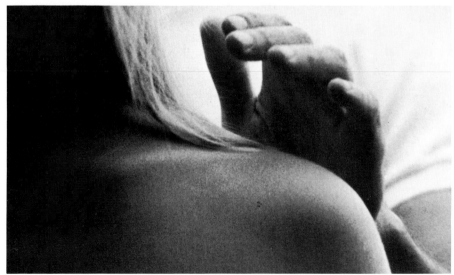

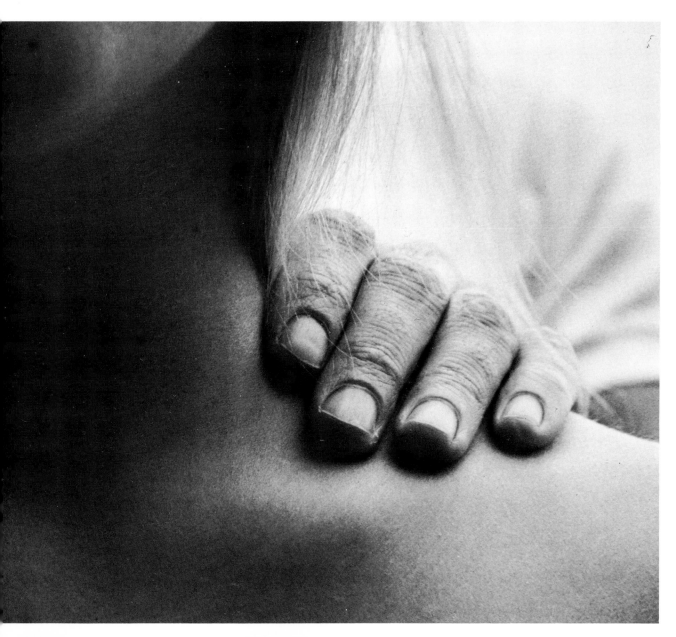

Shoulder Touching

Prelude: Shoulder Slapping.
Stand behind your partner.
Gently, firmly place both hands
on top of the shoulders
next to the neck.
Allow 30-40 seconds

for each touch
and 30 seconds between touches.
Stay alive in your hands.
Slowly take your hands away.
Give your partner enough time
to digest the effect
of this contact.
The second touch is on

the outer edge of the shoulders
still on top. The
final touch of the series is
in and around the
side-shoulder (deltoid muscle)
pressing gently
toward the mid-line of the body.

Move away slowly.
Give your partner a chance
to feel the effects.
Without talking,
he opens his eyes.
Exchange places.

Slapping

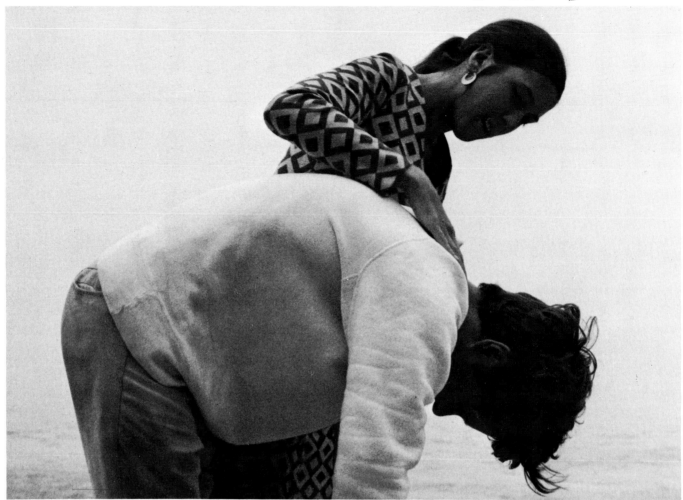

Back Bend Over and Slap

One partner bends over,
arms hanging down, fingertips
toward the ground, knees straight
but not locked. The other
person slaps vigorously the
entire back of his partner.
Include the side back and
buttocks. Go over the whole

72

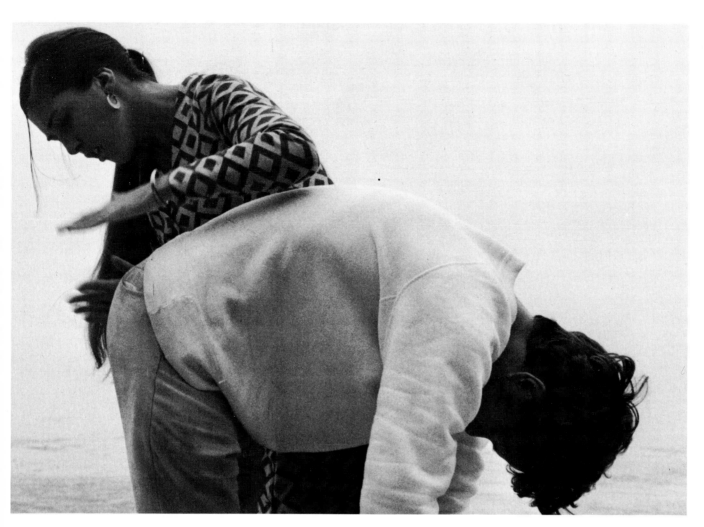

area 3 or 4 times. Slowly let
the slapping subside and move
away. The slapped partner
stays bent over and feels the
effects; and then stands up
slowly, one vertebra at a time,
taking at least 15-30 seconds,
and experiences his back. The
two change places.

Lifting

Giving Each Other a Lift (t)

Prelude: Back Body Slapping. The partner to be lifted settles on the floor on his back and closes his eyes. He neither hinders nor helps in the lifting process. If he tends to hold or help, the lifting partner non-verbally asks him to stop and let go. The lifting partner firmly grasps the lying partner's ankles and lifts the legs slowly to three-quarter position. Hold there for 10 seconds. Lower to the floor. Move away and let partner feel the effects. Then take hold firmly of the back of your partner's head (not the neck). Raise his head to three-quarter position. Hold there 10 seconds and then lower slowly. Remove your hands from under his head gently and gradually. Each lift should take at least 15-30 seconds. Lower in 15 seconds. Change places.

Slapping

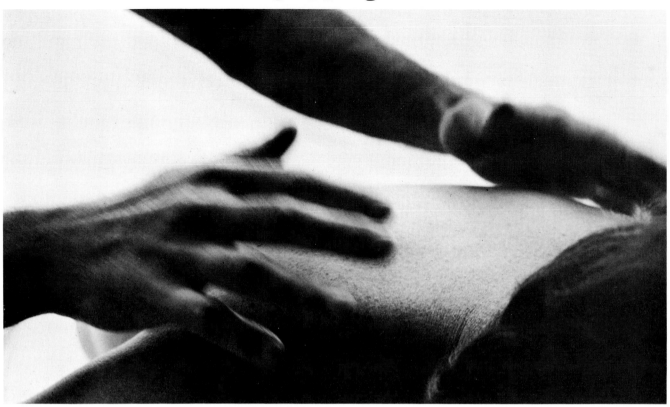

Back Slapping

The partner to be worked on
lies on his stomach.
He closes his eyes and
settles comfortably.
After giving him about 1 minute
to settle, the active partner
slaps his shoulders,
entire back, and buttocks.
Be sure to slap the side back.
The slap is vigorous
with lots of vitality but with no
punishment or pain.
Go over the whole area 3 times
and once over lightly.
After the slapping
allow your partner 30-45 seconds
to feel the effects.

Back Touching

Prelude: Back Slapping
The passive partner
lies on his stomach, closes his
eyes and settles comfortably.
The active partner
first applies his hands over
the area of the shoulder blades.
The two hands touch
simultaneously and lie flat,
but easy in position.
The toucher closes his eyes and
becomes aware of the breathing
movement under his hands.
After at least 30 seconds,
take your hands gently away.
The second touch is
in the area of the middle back.
The third touch
is on the lower spine.
Each touch lasts from 30-45
seconds, with 30 seconds
between each touch.
Notice where the breathing seems
to come from.
Be aware of how this touching
affects you. After the last touch
the passive partner opens
his eyes and you change
places without talking.

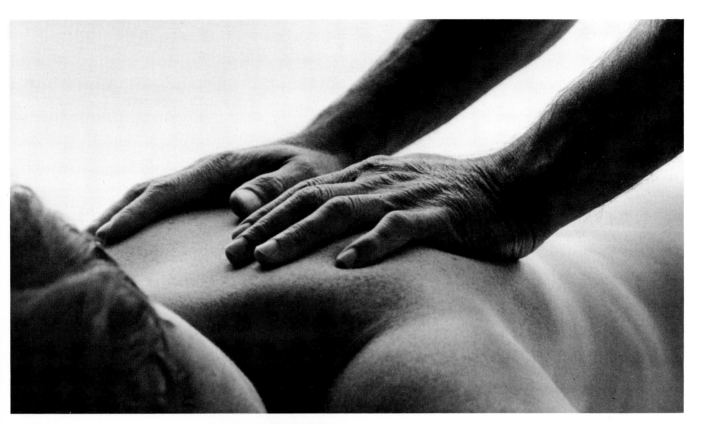

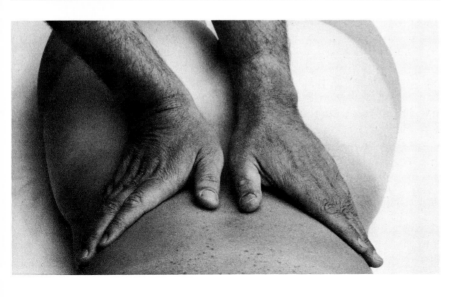

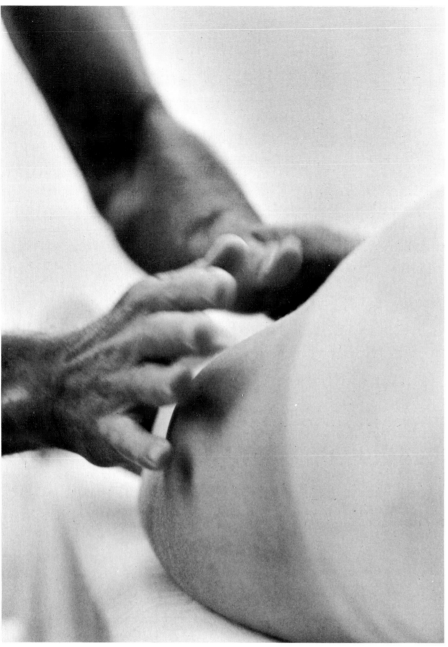

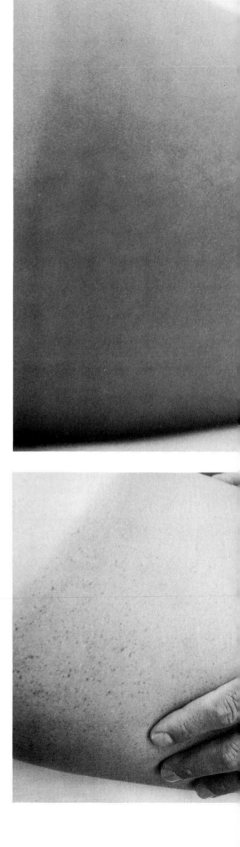

Back Leg Slapping

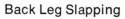

The passive partner
lies down on his stomach.
The active partner slaps
the lower half of the body
from the buttocks to the toes.
Slap both legs simultaneously.
Slap the side as well as the
back of the leg; include
the heel and bottom of the foot.
Go over the whole area completely
at least three times.
Move away and allow your partner
time to digest the effects.

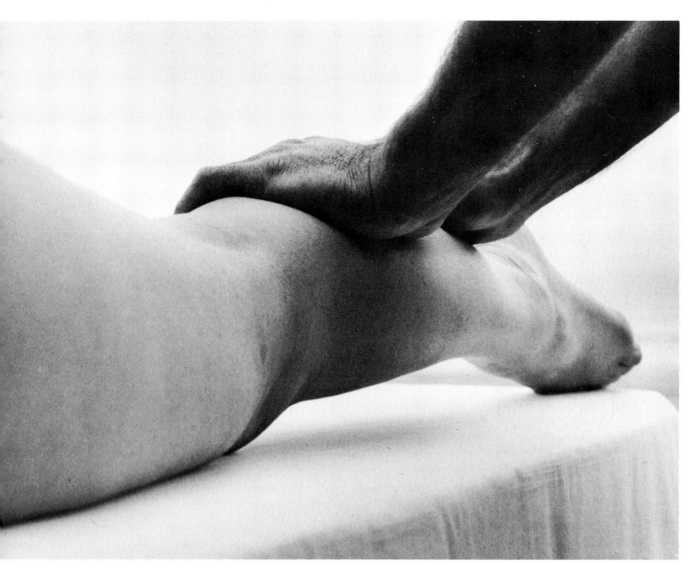

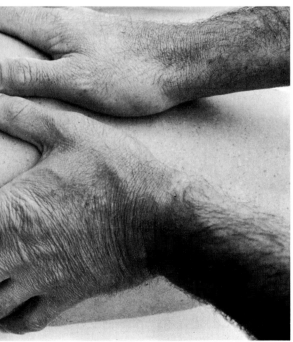

Back Leg Touching

Prelude: Back Leg Slapping.
The first touch is with
both hands over the buttocks.
The hands are gentle and firm
around the cheeks.
Allow 40 seconds for each touch,
moving slowly away each time.
Allow 30 seconds between touches.
In the second touch,
both hands enclose
the back of the left thigh.
In the third touch,
both hands are side by side over
the left calf.
Repeat the second and third
touches on the right leg.
Feel the after effects
of the touch.

Chapter 5
OPTIMAL TONUS

Relaxation is ease:
giving in, letting go.
letting in; open flow;
giving out.
The natural state
of the organism.
A condition in which nerves,
muscles experience
full sensation;
set their within tone;
without effort.

Ease, like digestion,
is not something you do;
it must be allowed.
Not letting go completely.
Sleepy-sagginess-collapse is
the opposite pole to
hyper-tension.
Rather being relaxed alive is
only the necessary
expenditure of muscular effort
desirable for
efficient functioning;
OPTIMAL TONUS.

Optimal tonus
is a dynamic concept
in which the organism
automatically adjusts
to the amount of muscular tension
necessary to perform
each particular act.
The best example is a cat,
sitting at ease,
completely alive, eyes
open or closed, breathing easily;
ready in an interested instant
to spring into action.
Complete involvement, absorption
in any activity or inactivity.
Never pushing or
straining unnecessarily.
No excessive effort,
allowing the organism to operate
with a minimum
of energy expenditure.
Muscles are firm-soft and
resilient, allowing coordination,
sensitivity, integrity.

Not restricted to animals
and children,
this kind of effortless ease
is displayed by master dancers,
athletes, craftsmen.

This kind of relaxation
permits activity with
decreased degeneration,
rest with
increased regeneration.
Proper respiration,
circulation, digestion,
elimination.
Improves health,
learning, living, loving.

Excessive tension, tautness:
a temporary emergency action.
The body's reaction; mobilization
for stress: combat or flight.
Occasional pressure-strain
is normal; to be in a continuous
state of chronic hypertension
is abnormal:
dis/order, dis/comfort,
dis/ease.

Some tension (muscle tone)
is desirable,
necessary to keep the body erect.
Certain activities
require more tone and energy:
sitting more than lying;
standing more than sitting,
walking more than
standing.

Children and animals
remain flexible;
after a situation is finished
their muscles readjust
by themselves
according to circumstance.
Most adults, reacting to symbols
and past situations
as well as the actual, over carry
their tension with them.
Their habitual tightening becomes
chronic, hindering sensitivity,
flexibility, productivity,
correct body functioning.

Paradoxically step one
in learning how to re-relax
is to become more aware of your
tension. Muscular tightness:
the shouting of your body
telling you to "stop tightening,"
to let it function.
Yes, telling you,
for the next step
is to experience, realize
that it is you
who are creating the tension.
Though it may be done
automatically, below the level
of consciousness,
it is still your own doing
(undoing). Step three:
discover, find out how you cause
and hold on to these tensions:
are you rigid in your chest
(depressing your breathing?);
are you exerting too much
pressure in your jaw
(afraid of biting someone's head
off?). The final stage is,
to "let go."
This giving up is
not done by avoiding tension
but by experiencing it;
moving toward and feeling,
being it.
Find out what it does for you.
If you really perceive and allow,
your tightening will
disappear.

The organism: mind/body
is a whole of interconnections.
Tension in one place
is reflected in others;
optimal tonus
in any area
makes it easier on the rest.
Certain spots
tend to be tension centers:
holding in the neck
to cut off body emotions:
disconnecting.
Tightness around the shoulders:
holding back
from striking out.
Rigid hips avoiding basic urges.
Suppressed breathing
to eliminate excitement.
Eyes straining
to see through everything.

Eye tension is subtle,
often unrealized.
It increases fatigue;
decreases efficiency, pleasure.
Pushing continuous staring
makes vision,
other areas of the body, hard.
Our eyes,
like all organs, work best
without excessive effort.
Seeing is allowing (eye opening).

Just by being more aware,
eye witnessing,
feeling, eye browsing
and letting go,
you will see a difference.

85

In some cases
tension binds muscles
so deeply, tightly
that they solidify.
Tissue de/generates, losing
its resiliency, elasticity, tone.
Some muscles shorten
while others lengthen
and the body alignment, balance
is destroyed,
literally putting a person
in bad shape.

For such advanced problems,
difficulties due to injury or
for higher order functioning,
the pioneering work of Ida Rolf
is recommended.
Called Structural Integration,
this deep musculo-fascia
manipulation brings about a
re/alignment, re/formation
of the entire organism.

Chapter 6
SENSORY AWAKENING

Man is energy: form flow.
Freed from excessive disturbance
he is life unlimiting;
increasing, able to perform.
Negative concepts
and chronic tension
causes fixation, solidification.
Excessive socialization,
injury, pressure
will deform the body,
create a lack of vitality:
energy, creativity blocked.
Through relaxation,
resensitization
the body can be re/formed,
trans/formed.

Sensory Awakening is
de-hypnosis,
a way out of rigid rules,
feelings, thoughts,
constrictions:
being tightly bound. An active
meditation: experiments,
exercises, and games designed
to quiet the overdominant
verbal pre-occupation of the mind,
to let go of chronic
excessive muscular tension
and focus consciousness
on direct sensory experience
in the here and now.

Sensory Awakening is
de-conditioning,
undoing: a method for turning off
your ego-centered mind
(those inner voices
which analyze, rationalize,
apologize, punish).

An aid to letting go;
open to effortless ease,
not trying; flow.
To relax, release, releasing:
optimal tonus.
Dynamic ease
based on body need.

A way to allow direct experience,
a return to primary process.
Unfiltered contact
with what is on going
without expectation
or excessive inhibition.
No sense of separation;
meditation, being in the now.
Oneness in
this happening moment.

warm breezes
in afternoon light
bright leaves
shaded grass
contrasting
streams of color
blend and discover
fuse and scatter
never to recover
this moment
ever again

Sensory Awakening is a process
for resensitizing the body
to heightened aliveness, being,
contact. To become
more conscious
of the rich potentiality within.
To redistribute consciousness
more evenly
over the entire organism.
To let go of automatic behavior;
to become more aware
of relationship and non-verbal
communication, body language,
posture.

The body being: breathing,
walking, reaching, touching;
infinite degrees
of feeling possibility.
Lightness-heaviness. The warm
flow of blood, the soft
liquid of the mouth.
No need to push, force,
the organism plays/works itself.
Effortlessly eyes see,
ears hear, noses smell, taste,
feel.

We are born sensitive,
are desensitized
and can resensitize.
Focus attention
on sensory experience, within-
without excessive strain.
Letting go of filtering
and habitual interference;
making contact with subtle life
movement, pleasure.

Non-verbal communication is:

Shaking hands
Your posture
Facial expressions
Your appearance
Voice tone
Hair style
Your clothes
Your gestures
The expression in your eyes
Your smile
How close you stand to others
How you listen
Your confidence
Your breathing
Your breath
Your manners
Your mannerisms
The way you move
The way you stand
How you touch other people

These aspects of you
affect your relationship
with other people, often
without you and them
realizing it.

The floor is not hard or soft
except in relationship;
standing against the floor
it will be hard against you.
For every action there is
an equal and opposite reaction.
Standing on or in the floor
is easy. Knowing this the
Japanese sleep on a bare floor.

Pushing eyes see hard and sharp,
causing eye strain,
fatigue, eyesolation. Easy eyes
the world is round, soft.
Forcing in elimination is
pushing the shit out of yourself,
symbolic of how you treat yourself in other areas.
Eating without chewing; trying
to swallow the whole world.
Afraid to breathe, to be alive,
to give in or out.

life is
breath taking
and giving

How you treat-mistreat;
deal or relate
with all the aspects of the
world/other
reflects your relationship
with yourself.

The body talks, its message
is how you really are,
not how you think you are.
Posture: do you
stand up for yourself?
Some people carry
the burden of the world
on their shoulders.
Others are so poorly balanced
that they can't stand
on their own two feet.
There are some girls
who lack support
and are push-overs. Many
in our culture
reach forward from the neck
because they are anxious
to get a-head. Others
hold their necks tight;
afraid to lose their head.
Look around you
at the poker faced
and the hard headed.

There are people who are tight,
hold back, non-giving,
tight assed. If the muscles
of the back are too weak
you don't have any back bone.
Stable bodies have
their feet on the ground.
Those who don't
experience their bodies
are very often unrealistic;
their heads in the clouds.
Others don't breathe
because they're scared to death.
Stoics keep a stiff upper lip;
unhappy people
are down at the mouth.

90

Body language is literal.
To be depressed is, in fact,
to press against yourself.
To be closed off
is to hold your muscles rigid
against the world. Being open
is being soft.
Hardness is being up tight,
cold separate,
giving yourself and other people
a hard time. Softness
is synonymous with pleasure
warmth, flow, being
alive.

Are you itching to get at
someone? Is your boss
a pain in the neck?
Are you sore about something?
What is your aching back
trying to tell you.
Is there someone on your back?
What about your ulcer?
Is there someone or thing
you can't stomach.
What is it that you'd like to
get off your chest?
Your body speaks to you
all the time, telling you
what your own needs are:
LISTEN here.

there's nothing special

about sensory awakening
about you

except

that you live on a big ball
in the midst of space.

that you can see, hear,

now
touch, taste, smell

flowers

sun, run, walk, sit, stand,
stretch, talk, sleep,

skin
feel
full

love
this is your birthright

because

It's enough
to be alive
to see the sea
the sky and
watch the changes
to eat talk
joke and create
love feel
the air ground
sun yourself
and not
have to
be somebody

Chapter 7
INSTANT SENSE

A series of micro-meditations.
A group of mini-
sensory experiences
to bring you into
the here and now.
Relaxing, awakening, stimulating
you out of the present tense
into ease.

Orange A-peeling

Take an orange
in the palm of your hand.
See its shape,
its color, its top and bottom,
the markings on the skin.
Smell the orange.
Close your eyes
and move the orange
in the palms of your hands.
Listen to the sound that your
hands make contacting it.
Take the orange and roll it
all over your face.
With your eyes closed,
feel the temperature of the
orange on your face.
Experience how your face feels.
Open your eyes and see
the orange. Sensitively
break the skin and begin to
peel the orange. See
the juice come out of the skin.
Hear the sounds.
Feel the breaking of the skin.
Watch it come apart.
See if you can keep the skin
together so that it
comes off in a large piece.
Watch the peeling being
torn away from the flesh of
the orange. Take time—listen
to the sounds. Look
at the inside of the peeling,
smell it. Look at the
flesh of the orange.
As slowly as you can, break
the orange in half and
watch it separate.
Slowly break off one section
and peel the skin off
in sections. Close your eyes
and eat that section
and the rest of the orange
one section
at a time.

Hand Washing

Close your eyes.
Become conscious of the whole
process of washing your
hands. Do it slowly.
Lather well. Feel the water.
Rinse and feel your skin.
Open your eyes.
Lather and rinse again, being
aware of all the details.
Dry your hands
and experience how they feel.

Variations: Rub your hands
with oil or cream.

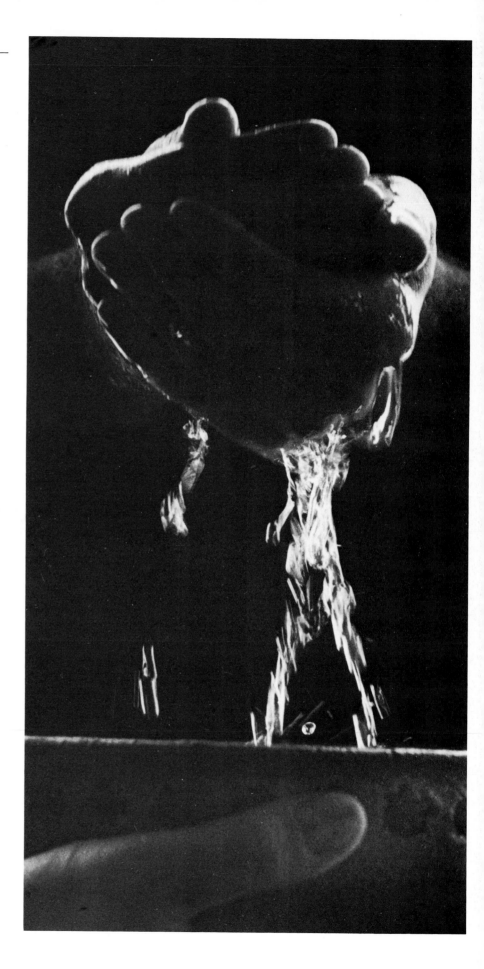

Attention to Here and Now

Close your eyes. Feel what your
feet are resting on.
Listen to the sounds in the room.
Experience your breathing.
Become aware of the air
surrounding your entire body,
especially the exposed areas,
the face and hands. Become
aware of the different articles
of clothing you are wearing
from the inside. Bring
your attention to your navel.
Then to the tip
of your nose.
With your eyes closed, experience
how you feel right now.
And then slowly
open your
eyes.

Mouth Washing

Close your eyes
and brush your teeth
for 3 minutes with great care.
Rinse and experience
your mouth.

Smoking a Cigarette

Become conscious of the entire
process of
lighting-smoking-putting out
a cigarette. How you take it out
of the pack, the sound of the
striking match,
the color of the flame,
the first puff, the smoke,
its color. Close your eyes and
experience bringing
the cigarette to your mouth,
the inhalation,
the exhalation.
Watch the tobacco paper burn,
pause between puffs,
even notice how you put
the cigarette out.
Close your eyes and be aware
of how you feel.

People often smoke compulsively
because they do not experience
and are not satisfied
by what they are doing.
Smoke less and enjoy more.

Stretch Your Body

Stand or lie on the floor,
close your eyes. Feel your body.
Without straining,
stretch every part
from your feet to your head;
Toes
Feet
Ankles
Calves
Knees
Thighs
Hips
Stomach
Chest
Arms
Hands
Fingers
Neck
Head
Your total body;
experience how you feel.
Open your eyes.

Sound Listening

Close your eyes.
Focus awareness on sound:
music,
in nature, on the radio,
or in a quiet room. Hear
the sound of the dishes being
washed, traffic, an airplane
passing by.

Your Subordinate Hand

For 30 minutes or longer
use your left hand exclusively if
your are right handed—or
vice versa if
you are left handed.
Do everything with your
weaker side as best you can.
Become aware of
your feelings—your patience
or lack of it.
How do you experience yourself
when the experiment is over?

A New Familiar Room

Go into a familiar room
and look at all the objects
in great detail,
one at a time. Look without
staring. Then see the room
as a whole,
from different angles,
points of view.

Blind Shower

Step in the shower and
close your eyes.
Shampoo your hair. Soap your
whole body. Rinse and dry
yourself completely before you
open your eyes.

Rock Experience

Find a rock the size
of your fist. Sit alone
in a quiet place.
Hold the rock in your hand.
Look at the rock. See its shape,
color, colors, the ridges
and indentations. Feel the weight
of the rock. Toss it
up and down in your hand.
Turn it over
and examine the other side.
Feel the surface of the rock.
Squeeze it and find out how
hard it is.
Close your eyes and rub the rock
over your face.
Experience its temperature,
its texture. Allow the rock to
settle gently over one
of your eye lids. Hold it there
for 30 seconds and then
take it away.
Experience that eye.
Cover the other eye lid
for 30 seconds with the rock.
Take the rock away.
Put your lips against the rock.
Let the rock rest anywhere
on your face.
leave it there for
from 30 seconds to 1 minute.
Place the rock on top
of your head for 1 minute.
Take the rock off and experience
how you feel. Open your eyes
and again see
the rock.

Being Breath

Close your eyes and for 3
minutes become aware of
your breath without interfering.
Then see if you can,
with your eyes closed, experience
its origin. Experience
the air moving in and out
of your nostrils.
Become aware of the whole cycle
of inhalation—pause—
exhalation—pause.
Feel the temperature of the air.
Allow your breathing process
to regulate itself.
Experience how you feel.
Open your eyes.

Hands Washing with Salt

Close your eyes
and wash your hands.
Take some ordinary table salt
and rub it gently
over the back and front of
the hands. Do each
of the fingers. Rinse, and feel
the skin. After drying
your hands, rub in some oil
or cream. Experience
how your hands feel.

A Sense Walk

Go for a walk
around a familiar block,
or someplace new, special. For
3 minutes concentrate
on the sounds around you.
For 3 minutes be aware
of the smells around you.
For 3 minutes touch everything
that you can
in your environment.
In the next 3 minutes see
everything around you
as if for the first time.
Now sit down and close your eyes.
Spend the next 3 minutes
on taste—for example,
smoke a cigarette,
chew some gum,
eat a piece of candy,
a piece of fruit—something you
really like.
Complete your walk,
keeping sense
activity in the foreground.
Allow yourself to experience
whatever presents itself.
See if you can
let sensations fuse and blend
into a total experience.

Chapter 8
TOUCH

Between indulgence and inhibition
is allowing;
letting go, letting be
being free
to permit or draw the line.
Permitting
without being permissive.
Permission to give yourself
the open possibility to move,
act or stay inactive
in relationship
to each ongoing experience,
situation, moment.

Awareness is spontaneous:
what is sensed.
Consciousness sensing around
what's going on
with/in with/out interference.
Experiencing,
not observing what's doing;
awareness is being ongoing.
Letting,
not making things happen;
being there,
aware.

110

Touch
is one of the basic languages
of muscles, nerves, love.
Mothers instinctively
touch their children
to comfort;
hold them close to relax
and reassure.
To be held is support;
to be touched is contact;
to be touched sensitively
is to be cared for.

Some people are touchy,
over sensitive,
don't like to be touched;
others are dying to be touched.
Being touched
is difficult for so many
because of the way
they were handled as children;
not really cared for.

Babies are easily touched,
love to touch.
To be touched is to be reached,
to feel and to be felt.
Touching and being touched
is a pleasure our culture
teaches us to keep away from.
Children and adults
from other societies
show more affection, animation;
touch much of the time.
Men walk down the street
holding hands, arm in arm
because they feel close
to one another.
In American culture
this is sometimes viewed
as a homosexual act.

In early civilizations
people clasped forearms
or embraced
in unselfconscious contact,
exchanging the life energy,
creating a bond.
Today we shake hands
at arms length or embrace
with our shoulders and face,
avoiding real contact.

Touch and pleasure
can be sensuous
without being sexual.
There is a great amount
of communication, caring,
close openness
which can come
in mutual sensory interaction;
satisfaction.

Hugging and kissing
is usually confined
to the immediate family
or to courtship. We learn
to not express our selves,
to be reserved, cool.
In a trip to Europe,
Sidney Jourard
counted the number of times
friends made physical contact
while talking, the average
was about 100 times an hour.
Returning to the mid-West
he again took up the count.
The average went down
to 3 touches per hour.
Is it any wonder that
so many Americans are
out of touch?

Physical contact can be curing,
reassuring;
inspire desire or good will;
create peace and release.
Convey a sense of sharing,
understanding, ease,
pleasure or anger.

Touch
has always been
a most effective method
of healing. The energy
that flows through the hands
can refresh, regenerate,
revitalize.
The laying on of hands
can create great
physical-mental changes.
In the hands of a person
who understands, touch
sometimes can be as effective
as drugs or surgery.

Sensitive touching
is both firm and gentle,
giving;
a helping hand
creates confidence.
Relating to the situation,
the individual,
your real feelings,
feeling
rather than technique.

Each person has his own touch,
like his own voice
or personality.
Some are grabbers,
crushers, rushers, heavy handed.
Others uncomfortable,
avoid by touching lightly,
with sweaty, clammy palms.
Still others
are dead in their hands,
without feeling,
disconnected
between their shoulders
and hands
Arm muscles held rigid
too hard to feel.

Becoming
comfortable with touch
requires patience and awareness.
Experience
what your attitudes are,
how you touch,
what your feelings are.
Slowly, if you desire,
you can change these reactions
and allow yourself to
enjoy touching
not only others,
but the floor, yourself,
paper, food, trees,
animals, flowers,
life.

Chapter 9
INTIMATE GAMES

The following games
are for married-engaged couples
who wish to get to know
re/know each other better.
Partners who want to become
more familiar,
whose desire is to take care,
grow, explore, share
their vast limitlessness.

These experiences
can lead to sexual arousal,
though this is not their only
or main purpose.
One must be careful
to experience the impulse
rather than label sensations.
Because of past associations
touch feelings
which are pleasurable
are mis-categorized as sexual.
There is a huge difference
between sensuousness
and sexuality. Sensuousness
is an appreciation-delight
in light, texture,
color, sound, flavor; the
continuous play of the senses.
Sexuality is a small
but important part
of the sensuous life.

One of the difficulties
with sexuality
is that it very often takes place
between people who are
just getting acquainted or
who think they know
all about each other. Sexual
intercourse in our culture
is usually the last act
in the evening when
one or both parties are tired.
Having a climax is overstressed
and there is seldom
enough time concern
for petting, foreplay,
after play.

When doing
the following experiments
remember
love is care
care for one another
carefully.

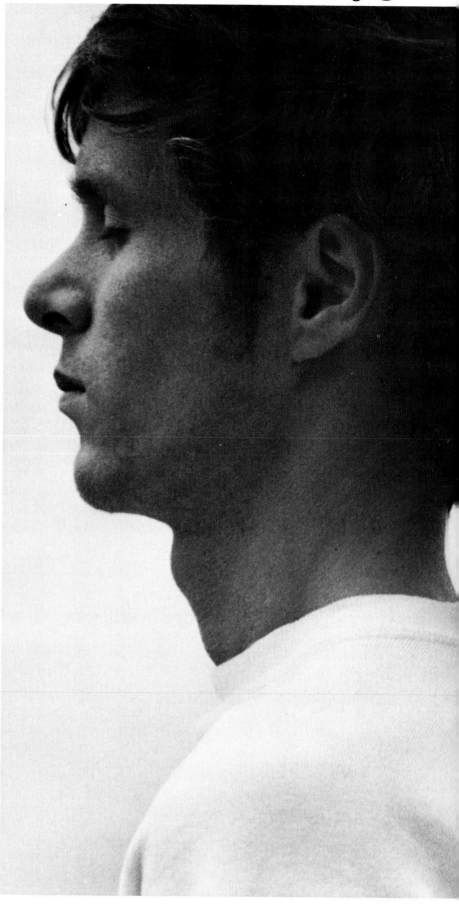

Back Talk

Prelude: Back Slap-Touch.
After both backs are slapped,
the couple stands back to back
with eyes closed,
and through movement
get to know each other's backs.
Have a non-verbal conversation
with your backs. (One person
rubs; the other listens; take
turns.) Have a back argument.
Make up. Be very gentle,
playful. Move up and down at
various speeds. Eventually stand
quietly back to back and
slowly separate.
Experience your back—
how you feel.
Turn around, open your eyes
and see your partner.

Touching

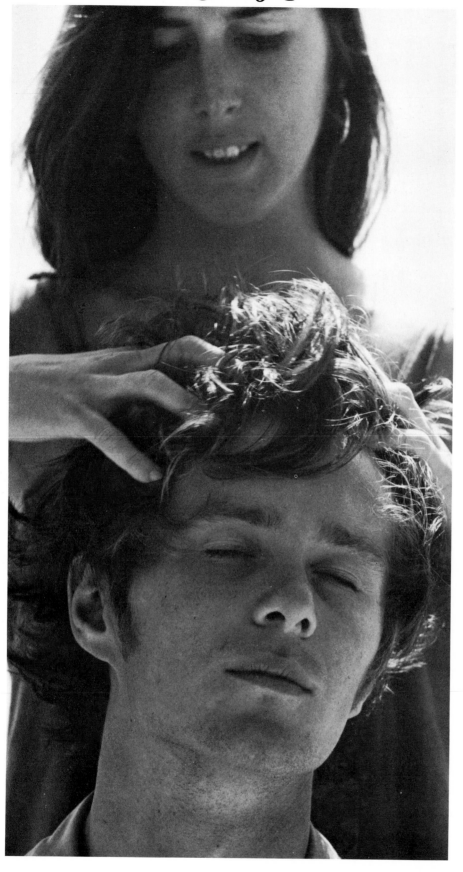

Head Knowing

Prelude: Head Tapping-Slapping.
Have your partner close
his eyes. Stand
behind him, close your eyes
and gently get acquainted with
your partner's head, hair,
back of the neck, ears.
Use very soft strokes, caresses.
Take your time,
get to feel-know the whole
area thoroughly.
Now open your eyes and continue
your exploration. Be aware
of the hair: colors, texture.
Let the hands go, flow, dance
all over his head.
When you move away, let your
partner experience the effects.
Change places.

Palm Dance

Prelude: Arm-Shoulder Slapping.
Stand facing your partner,
elbows up and touching palms.
Palms stay together during the
entire experience; eyes closed.
With your palms together
have a conversation-dance.
First one partner leads,
then the other, until it is
just happening by itself.
Now, have an argument in your
palm dance. Make up gradually
and be gentle with one another.
Then do a happy fun dance.
Dance as if you were in love.
Speed up or slow down the dance;
let the dance expand (increase
your range of movement).

Slowly let the dance subside.
Remain palm to palm, eyes closed.
Now, after 30 seconds, one
partner takes 1 large step back
(one foot) and leans forward
at the shoulders, letting his
partner support his weight.
After 30 seconds, change places.
After another 30 seconds,
both partners take 1 large step
back and mutually support each
other for 30 seconds. Remaining
in this position, open your eyes
and see one another.
After 30 seconds, close your eyes
Slowly stand up, separate, and
experience how you feel.
If it is desirable, discuss the
experience with your partner.

Slapping

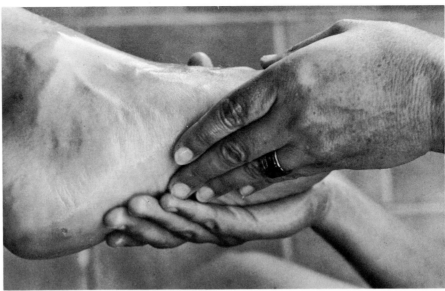

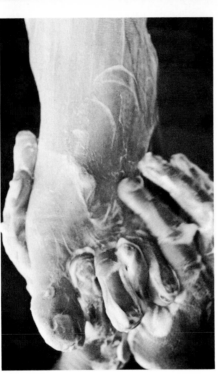

Foot Washing

Prelude: Foot Slapping-Noting.
Fill a large bucket or
pan with warm water and slowly,
sensitively,
wash your partner's feet.
At times one or both partners
close their eyes.
After washing the foot well,
take some wet table salt and rub
it over the entire foot,
especially over the dead skin.
Rinse and feel
your partner's foot.
Then dry and take some oil and
rub it into the foot.
Let your partner feel his
feet and then have him walk on
them. Change places.

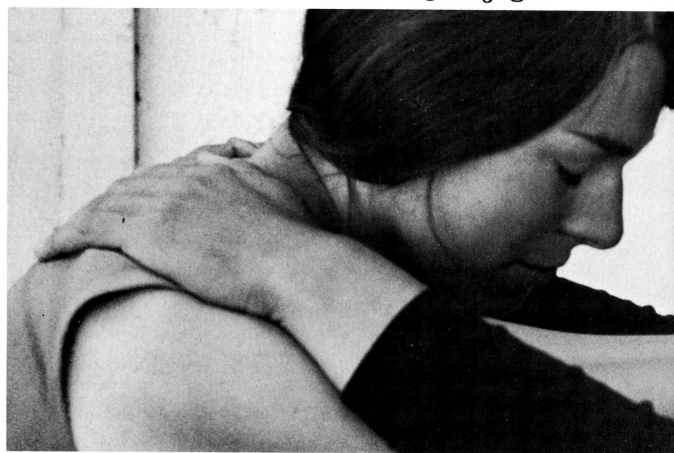

Hand and Arm Shoulder Dance

Prelude: Shoulder Arm Slapping.
Sit on the floor next
to one another, knee to knee.
Close your eyes
and take each other's hands.
Explore and get to know
one another's hands, the backs
as well as the palms.
Become familiar with the fingers.
Feel—experience—be aware.
Now allow your exploration
to include each other's wrists—
get to know these wrists.
Include the forearm to the elbow,
discovering the feelings
and sensations in this area.
Now include the upper arm

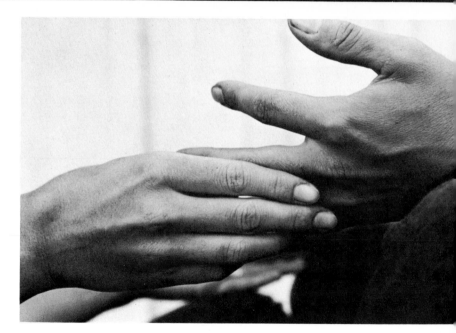

and eventually the shoulders,
moving over and around.
Try different movements,
different degrees of pressure,
using different parts
of the hand, fingers, and nails.
Spend at least 3 minutes
on each part, keeping the eyes
closed the entire time.
Now go back to holding
each other's hands quietly
for a few moments.
Slowly open your eyes
and see each other. Express
non-verbally to your partner
how you feel about him.

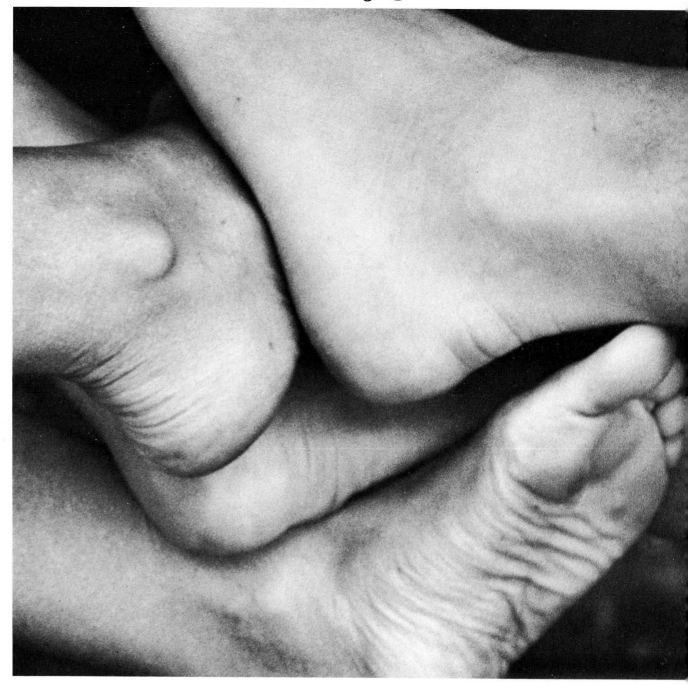

Foot Slapping

Find a comfortable position
to slap your partner's feet,
like sitting on the floor.
Simultaneously slap the top
and bottom of one foot
with both hands.
Slap the sides of the foot.
With one hand slap the heel and
bottom of the foot.
Go over the entire foot
with both hands.
Gently and gradually let
the slapping subside.
Take your hands away.
Let your partner feel the
effects of the slap.
Slap the other foot.
Change places.

Foot Conversation

Prelude: Foot Slapping.
Both partners close their eyes
and lie on their backs on
the floor. Bending their knees
they put their feet together in
mid-air. Experience your feet
touching. Begin to have a
non-verbal conversation
with your partner's feet.
One partner says something with

128

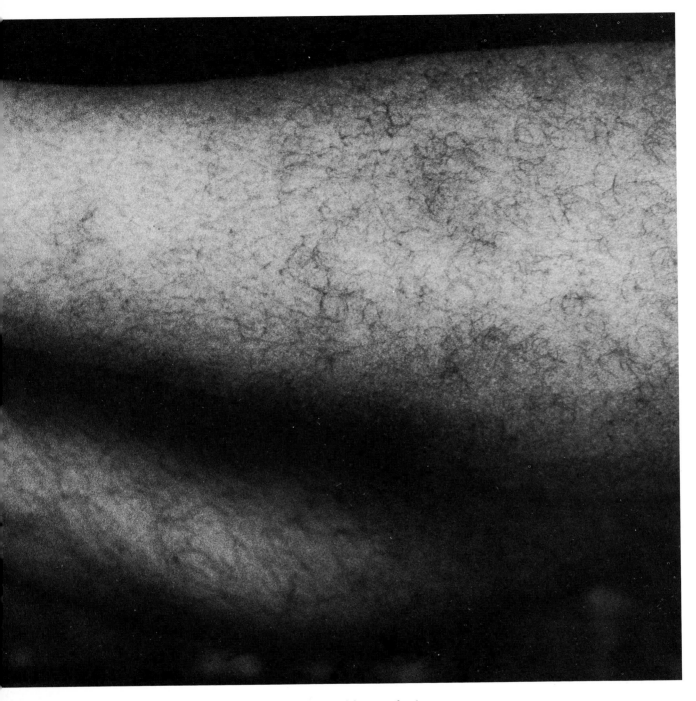

his feet and the other answers.
After 1 minute, have
an argument with your feet.
Then gradually begin to
make up. Now be gentle with
each other's feet. Next do a
happy playful foot dance.
Find various ways to
experience-explore
each other's feet. Slowly let
the movement subside.
Feel your feet together.

Say good-bye with your feet
to your partner's feet
and slowly separate.
Put your feet on the floor.
Experience how they feel.
Open your eyes.

Touching

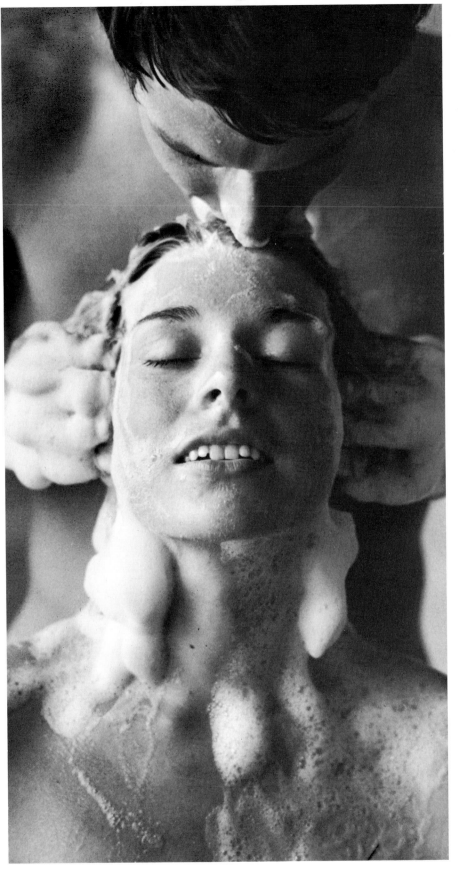

Exchange Shampoos

Prelude: Head Tap-Slap.
Have your partner
keep his eyes closed
during this entire experience.
Give him a complete shampoo.
Get a pitcher or jar so
that you can pour water over him.
Periodically close your eyes
while working on your partner,
feeling the head, soap suds—
wetness. Rinse and dry the
hair with a towel.
Run your hands through his hair,
comb it, smell it.
Change places.

Touching

Face Slapping and Knowing

Slap-pat your partner's face.
Move away and allow him to
digest the effects.
Now close your eyes and
with your hands explore—
get to know your partner's face.
After 3 minutes
open your eyes and
continue the exploration
with eyes open.
After another 3 minutes make
any finishing touches that might
be desirable and move away.
Your partner remains
with eyes closed, feeling the
effects of the experience.
Take a look at his face
to see how
it has changed. The
partner opens his eyes. After
a couple of minutes change roles.
After both partners are done,
close your eyes and
rub your faces together.

Variation: Run a flower over
your partner's face.

Head Slapping

Prelude: Head Tapping.
Stand behind your partner.
The front partner
closes his eyes. With your
fingers, slap over the top
of your partner's head;
the back of his head,
the sides, the forehead. Remain
in each area about 15 seconds.
If there is
a particular spot on the head
he would like to have worked on,
he points to it.
After this and some more general
slapping, go gently
over the whole area.
Slowly and gradually
let the slapping subside.
Move away. Allow
30-45 seconds for your partner

to feel the effects.
Come around and look
at your partner's face.
What changes, if any,
have occurred?
Change places with your partner.

Bathing Together

Prelude: Body Slapping.
Slap each other over the entire
body from head to toe.
Take a shower or tub together.
Without rushing,
sensitively take turns
washing each other's body,
sudsing every inch.
Rinse and dry one another.
If the situation permits, oil and
massage each other.

Variation:
Take a bubble bath together.

remember
love is care
care for one another
carefully.

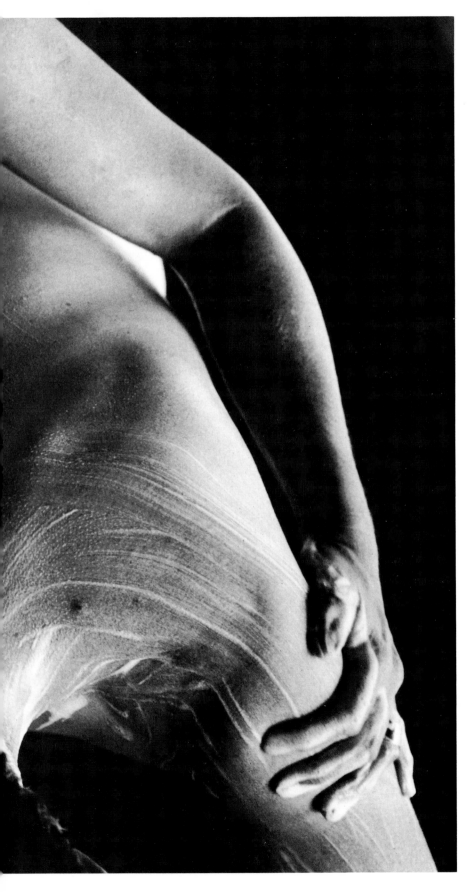

Chapter 10
APPLICATIONS

Sensory Awakening
like true meditation,
education, religion,
can be an integral part
of each rich moment life.
A process that can involve
every activity; relationship.
A sensible open method
that can be intelligently applied
as an enhancing adjunct
to therapy, teaching, creativity
leisure, housework, worship.

Meditation
(effortless concentration)
can be contemplation
inwardly focused
or being absorbed in action.
Like the Zen ways of liberation,
meditation can be everything:
eating, walking, breathing,
painting, loving.

Sensory Awakening
is active meditation:
the open experiencer
becomes the experience.
Satisfying in themselves,
these sensory experiments
can also be used as a warm-up,
prelude to sitting meditation.
Through optimal toning
into awareness
sitting becomes easier,
the mind/body quieter,
the concentration
involvement deeper.

By following awareness principles,
housework can be more
than just a chore. Before
starting activities
do a few
of the awakening experiments
(those which you feel
most in need of)
then begin work.
With a reflective attitude
dust becomes patterns
rather than dirt,
the job an experience
not just a task,
something to get over with.

The next time you do dishes,
be sensitive to shapes,
temperatures, textures,
bursting soap bubbles.
Get rid of your expectations—
it's going to be a drag;
I'm not going to enjoy this—
and allow yourself to be
wholly aware.

Creativity
is being yourself,
expressing.
Not a forced task,
but an over out flowing
of the unique you.
Each of us is uniquely gifted;
but most people wrap their
presents
in a tightly restricting,
conforming personality box,
creativity blocked.

The procedures in this book
can help bring you out
from under wraps
and knock your
block off.

sleeping
nature
unlocks

jack out
of
the box

spring

Leisure can be active
or being quiet; inactive.
Doing or non-doing
just for the fun of it;
for its own sake.
In the electric age
machines replace man producing;
more free time.
Time is a construct
we impose on infinity;
being is full participation:
timeless.
Much of the time
we waste time,
kill time, spend time.
Suspend time
in the relaxed now;
contemplation
in every moment
activity;
giving yourself:
time.

Psychotherapy has moved
away from talk,
dealing with the past,
analysis: lack of involvement.
The direction is toward
experience, encounter,
staying in the here and now
in an I-thou relationship.
Away from insight
and into experience;
leaving the head orientation
for a total mind/body approach.

Sensory Awakening
offers direct assistance
in enhancing individual,
family and group therapy.
A way to physically deal
wth diagnosis, personality,
resistance, anxiety
and depression.
Numerous experiments in trust,
support, affection, anger,
relating, caring, touching.
Literally,
methods for helping people
to keep in touch with reality.

Education ideally is
an active, interested exploration:
skill, learning, knowing,
doing. Too much
of formal education
is dulling memorization, passive
compartmentalization,
indoctrination.

The initiation
of sensory training in education:
to sit properly, stand
naturally, move freely.
To relax the body
is to be more open minded,
learning to read without strain,
study without excessive pressure,
to develop a richer, more complete
psyche/physical self.

Art and anatomy can be
taught by feeling and
identification.
Chemistry is cooking,
digesting food.
Understanding body messages
a new/old language.
Music listening, participation
with the entire organism.
Geology is a sensitivity
for the earth, gravity,
relationship.
Supplementary
non-verbal methods
could help expand
schooled learning
from every point of you.

Religion is the attempt
on the part of people
who have had peak experience
to share those experiences
with non-peekers . . . . Maslow

Worship: contact
with the ground of being:
life unity mystery.
A part not apart of existence.
Pouring the wine
need not be anybody's blood;
it's divine by its very substance.
Fill your cup, feel
its weight, taste its flavor,
pass it to,
see your neighbor.

The breaking of bread,
not anyone's flesh,
the miracle is
right before your eyes,
ears, nose, mouth.
Forget the abstractions
and chew, true communion:
love sacred, sharing contact,
caring for yourself,
for others.

The washing of feet,
the laying on of hands,
relaxation and
other sensory experiences can
help bring ritual,
religion back to life.

Chapter 11
GROUP GAMES

Slapping

opening
to a group
with self awareness experiments,
followed by couples,
small and large group activity;
creates a bond
of unseparateness
that is enhancing
to group, self,
individual joy
dancing.

146

Shaking

Shaking Up
_____

Prelude: Shoulder Slapping.
The group walks
interweaving
between one another.
Start shaking both the hands
of each person you meet.
Now shake each other's elbows.
Then shake
one another's shoulders.
Continue this shaking procedure
on each others hips, legs,
heads, ears and noses.
Do each activity for at least
15-30 seconds. After,
close your eyes
and experience how you feel.

We all conform by shaking hands.
What about the rest of the body?
Why not give it a fair shake?

Touching
Hand to Hand

Prelude: Shoulder Slapping.
Walk interweaving between
one another shaking right hands.
At some point, stop, take hold
of someone's right hand and,
eyes closed, touch-explore this
right hand. After 2 minutes hold
hands, open your eyes and
see your partner. Now, move about

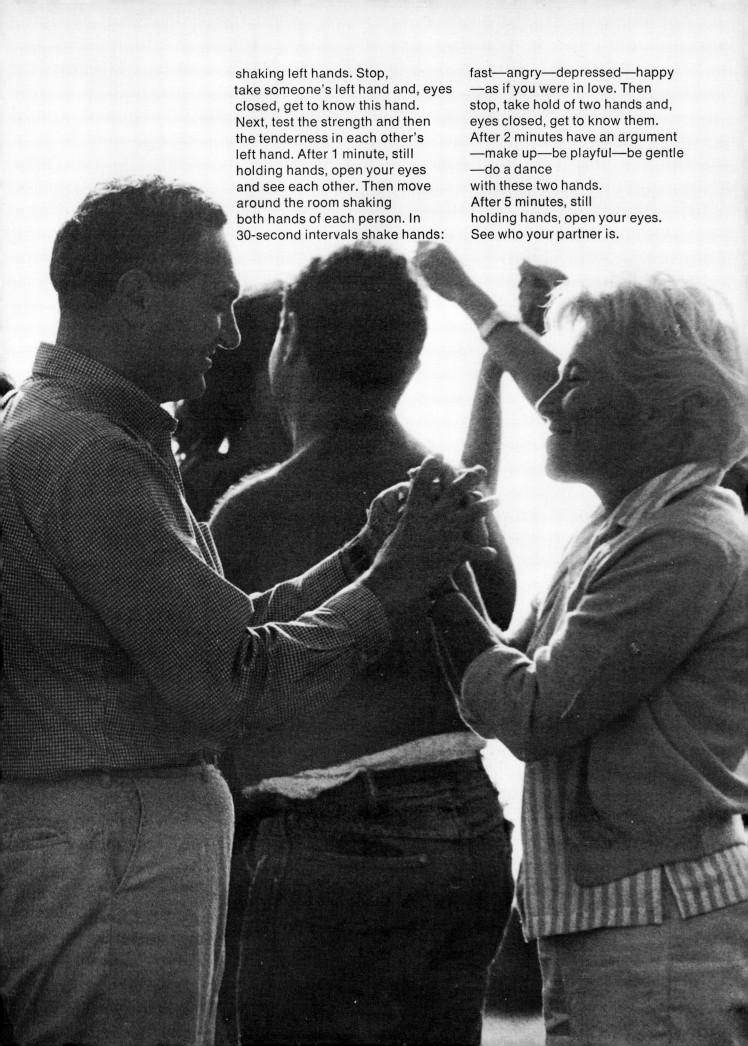

shaking left hands. Stop,
take someone's left hand and, eyes
closed, get to know this hand.
Next, test the strength and then
the tenderness in each other's
left hand. After 1 minute, still
holding hands, open your eyes
and see each other. Then move
around the room shaking
both hands of each person. In
30-second intervals shake hands:

fast—angry—depressed—happy
—as if you were in love. Then
stop, take hold of two hands and,
eyes closed, get to know them.
After 2 minutes have an argument
—make up—be playful—be gentle
—do a dance
with these two hands.
After 5 minutes, still
holding hands, open your eyes.
See who your partner is.

Back Knowing

Prelude: Back Slapping.
Eyes closed, each person
sensitively backs in toward the
center of the room.
As you do make contact with
other backs, gently bump hello
and move on. After 1 minute
stop next to one back and
get to know this back with your
back. After a couple of minutes,
separate; one partner turns
around and with his hands, eyes
remaining closed, gets to know
his partner's back. After
2 minutes, change places. Now
move back to back again
and in 30-second intervals have:
a back conversation
—and argument
—be playful—be tender;
do a back dance staying together,
exploring all kinds of motion.
After 5 minutes stop and be aware
of each other. Then,
slowly and gradually move apart.
Experience how your back feels;
then open your eyes and
see your partner.

Slapping

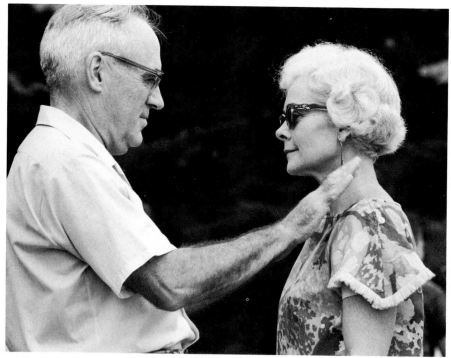

Slapping Conversation

Prelude: Shoulder Slapping.
Partners face each other.
The area to be slapped is over
the entire arms and shoulders,
including the backs
of the hands and fingers.
Without verbalizing, one partner
starts the conversation
by slapping (with both hands
simultaneously).
The other partner answers.
This goes back and forth
like ordinary conversation.
Don't try to be logical.
Try to say different things
by changes in tempo.
Don't hog the conversation.
Sometimes talk to one area;
other times talk
to the whole area.
Don't talk (slap) too loudly
or too softly. Have a
slapping argument (not too wild).
Gradually make up.
Slap something tender.
Say something funny
in slap talk. Slap
each other "so long." Close
your eyes and feel the effects
of this type of conversation.

Passing in a Circle

Prelude: Back Slapping.
One member of the group
stands in the center of a closed
circle. He closes his
eyes, knees straight, feet
together. His entire body is
reasonably stiff (not rigid) and
he falls back.
He is caught and passed around
the circle, or across the circle
at different speeds, in different
directions. After the passing,
the receiving person is put in
the center of the circle and
enclosed by all the members
of the group. After 30 seconds,
the group slowly moves away,
leaving him standing alone
in the middle of the circle.
This is a small group activity
for from 6 to 8 members.

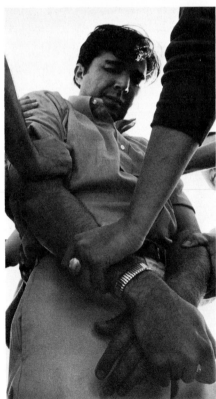

160

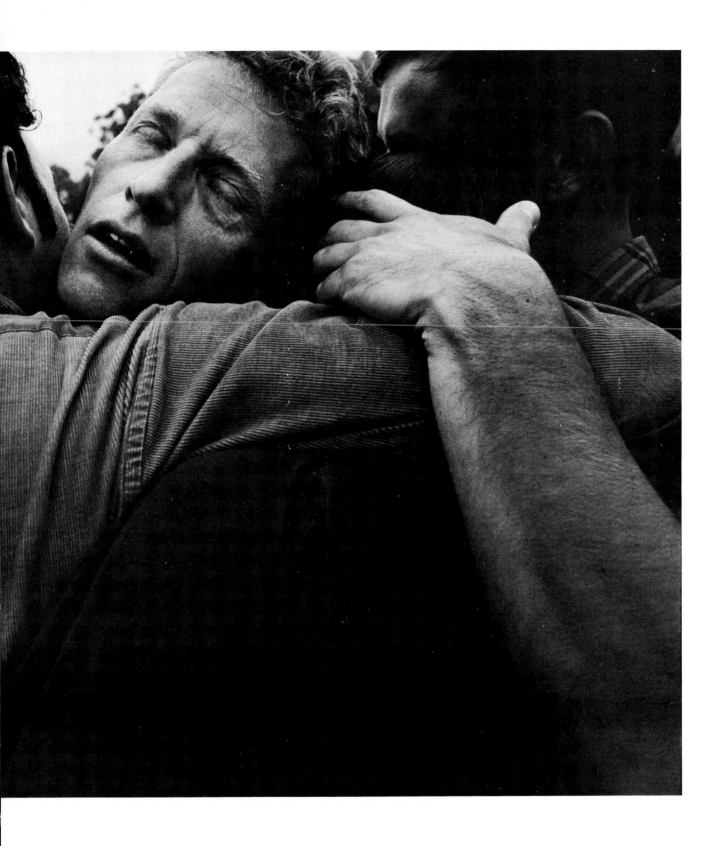

Exploring

The Blind Walk

Prelude: Tapping-Slapping.
After taking a partner,
one person closes his eyes
and the other person leads him
by the arm on a 10- to 30-
minute blind walk.
There is no talking
during the entire experience.
The person leading the walk
has his partner touch, smell,
feel and have as many interesting
experiences as possible:
have him feel a flower;
have him feel another person;
roll in the grass;
put his hand in some water;
let him get to know a rock.
Vary speeds; dance together.
After the allotted time,
switch places.
When both partners have
experienced the walk, sit down
and talk about your experiences
with each other.

Lifting

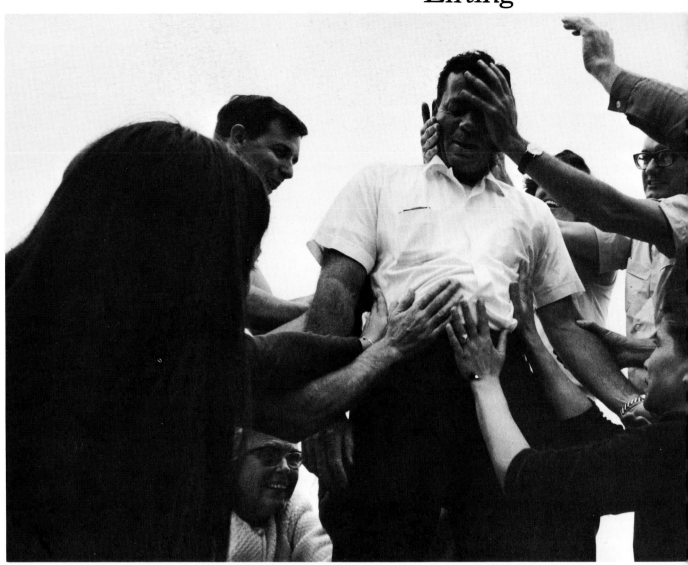

Group Lift

Prelude: Back Slapping.
One person lies on his back,
closes his eyes.
The rest of the group kneels
around him and slowly
putting their hands under his
body, the group lifts
(cradles) him gently. Any or all
of the following may be done:
swing (fast or slow),
run around at varying speeds,
lift overhead, turn him over,
throw him into the air and catch.
Carefully, put the person
down. Let him feel the effects.
Repeat on each group member.

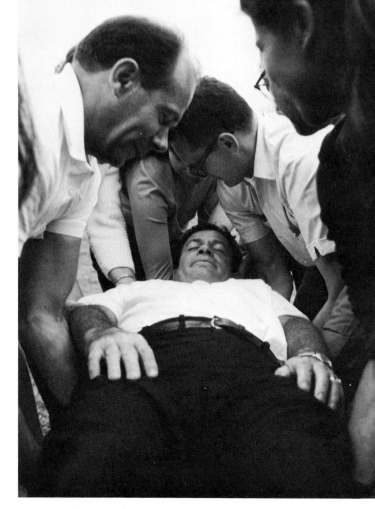

Crawling

Crawling onto a Pile

Prelude: Group Activities.
The group lies on their bellies
in a large circle.
heads pointing toward the center.
With eyes closed they begin
crawling toward the center.
At times, you will contact
others, possibly even
crawl over others. It is
important to be sensitive and
careful. Continue to crawl until
you reach the center pile.
Don't let the pile get too high.
At different points in
the process, stop and experience
what you are touching.
how you feel.
When the pile is complete,
stay in position.
Open your eyes
and see one another
Slowly unpile.

Touching Hands in a Pile

Prelude: Hand to Hand.
The group (up to eight) forms a
circle, shoulder to shoulder.
One person puts a hand
in the center of the circle.
Another member's hand
goes on top of the first.
Repeat until each person has both
hands in the circle. After
all hands have joined

the pile, everyone closes
his eyes. Become aware of your
feelings. The hand on the
bottom of the pile comes to the
top of the pile. The next bottom
hands move up and so on.
Speed can be varied from fast to
slow. Have someone
pour some oil on the hands
as they continue to move.
Move hands in other directions,
outwards, circles, etc.

Squeeze hands.
Explore the variety of movements
possible without losing contact
with the center pile.
Finally, slide hands
slowly out of the center of the
circle, simultaneously
or one by one.
Experience your hands,
yourself.
Open your eyes.
Look at the group.

Exploring

Under the Sheets

Prelude: Group Activities.
Each person goes under
a sheet and stays
quiet for 5 minutes.
They are allowed
to do anything they want to,
except to move
around the room. Then
move about the room,
contact/encounter other people

or groups
as long as each stays under
his own sheet.
Be open to your desires and
let whatever action-reaction
that wants to happen
occur. No talking during the
experience. When it is
over, experience how you feel;
come out from under your sheet.

OM

This chant-sound
is divided into two syllables.
On the first half of the
exhalation, you make the sound
"O," as in "ocean."
On the last half of the
exhalation, you make the sound
"mm," as in "dome."
The group stands together in a
circle, arms around each other's
shoulders, eyes closed.
Together the members
of the group
take a deep breath.
As they let out the air
together, they say
the first syllable
(loudly and with feeling).
Half-way through, they switch
to the second syllable.
Don't try to prolong the second
syllable. When you run out
of breath, just stop.
Allow 10-20 seconds
between chants.
Chants may be repeated three, six,
or any number of times.

Variations: The women
in the group chant first
and are answered by the men.
Varying degrees of counterpoint
may be created.

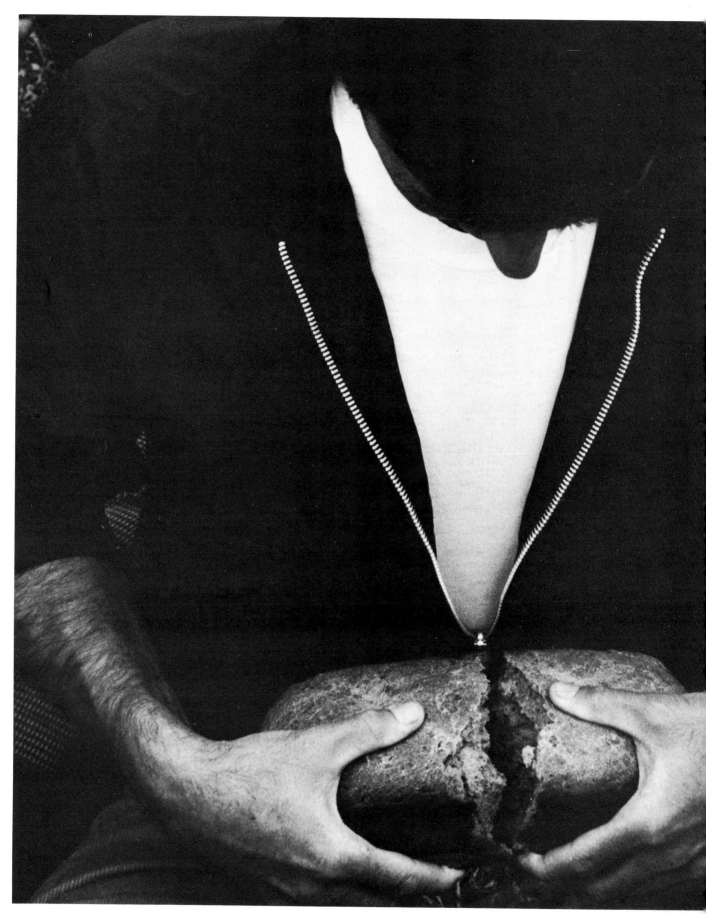

Tasting

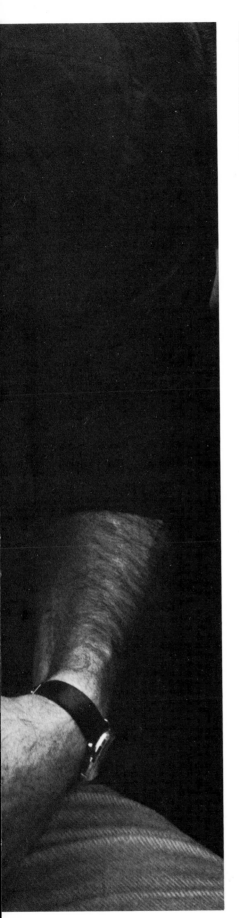

Bread Ceremony

Prelude: Group Activities.
Sit in a circle surrounding a loaf
of unsliced bread.
After sitting quietly, looking at
the bread, pass it around the
circle. Allow each person to feel
its weight and smell its flavor.
As the loaf is passed from one
person to another, look into each
other's eyes. One person
slowly (just a fraction of an inch
at a time) breaks the bread open.

The group watches. The
two halves are passed around
the circle, each person
looking at the inner exposed half
and breaking off a piece no
bigger than he can chew
comfortably. After each person
has taken his piece of bread, he
closes his eyes. He puts the
bread in his mouth and
slowly chews, not swallowing
until the bread is completely
liquefied. Afterward open your
eyes and see all of the group.

Slapping

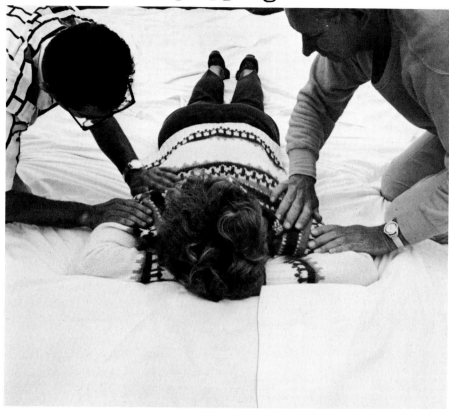

Two Slap One

The passive partner
of this trio lies down
on his stomach.
The other two partners sit
one on each side of him.
Simultaneously they slap
the entire back
including the buttocks.
Gently go over the whole area.
Give your receiver time
to digest the effects
of the slapping. Now slap his
buttocks, legs and feet.
Be sure you both stay
in a corresponding position
as you slap.
After a vigorous slap, gently
go over the whole area.
Gradually
let the slapping subside.
Move away and let your partner
feel the effects
Change places.

Gunther Sandwich

Prelude: Two Slap One.
The person just slapped
turns on his side.
One of the slappers lies
down on his side;
the front of his body against
the first partner's back.
His arm goes around his partner's
waist. The remaining member of
the group lies on his side,
his back touching the front of
the middle partner.
The middle person puts his arm
around the front partner's waist.
Experience one another,
your breathing.
After 1 minute the back person
slowly and gradually leaves.
After 15-30 seconds
the front partner moves away.
After feeling the effects,
switch places.

Touching

Group Back Slapping

One member of the group
lies down on his stomach.
The rest of the group
surrounds him kneeling.
Arrange yourselves in pairs
on opposite sides.
All slapping should be done in
the same approximate areas
on opposite sides of persons
across from each other.
If there is an odd number,
one member can position himself
at the head or feet. The person
being slapped does nothing
except receive
the gift of the hands.
Slap the entire body;
back, arms, buttocks, feet.

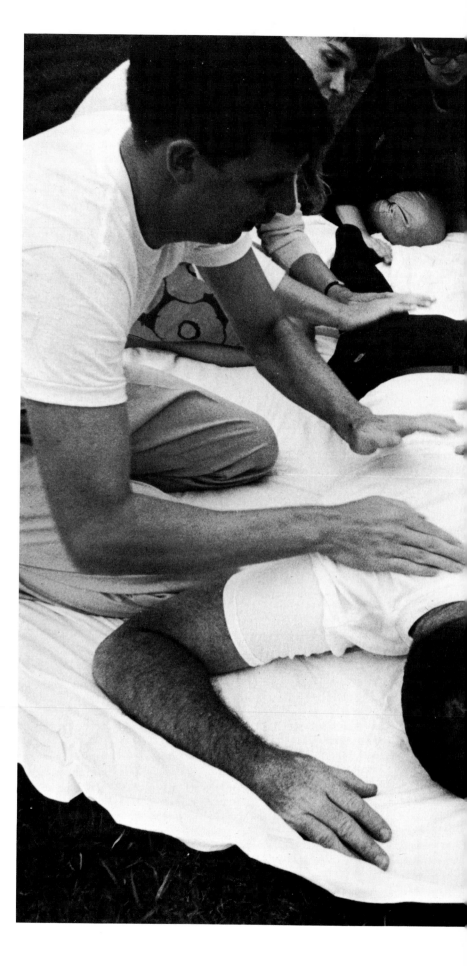

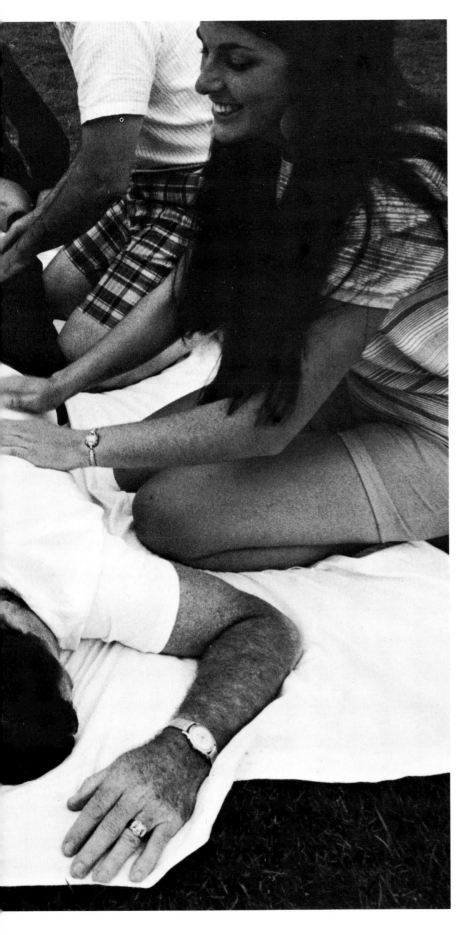

Stop and allow him to absorb
the effects.
This may be followed by

the Laying On of Hands.
Allow 30 seconds
after back slapping.
The group applies their hands
simultaneously over the entire
back of the body.
The touch is gentle, without
pressing or leaning.
The application lasts from
10-60 seconds.
This process may be repeated
two or three times
allowing digestion time
between touches.
Allow time afterwards
for the receiver to
feel full effects.

Seeing

Group Seeing Eyes

Prelude: Group Activities.
The entire group forms a
long line and holds hands.
The person at one end starts a
snake-like chain of movements in
which he doubles back so that as
he moves by the group and
they move by him, they are facing
each other. As people go by
at various distances, they look
in each other's eyes. The
group moves at different speeds,
gradually slows down, forms a
circle, and closes its eyes.
After taking 30 seconds
to experience how they feel,
they open their eyes and
again look at one another
as a group.

Gunther Hero Sandwich

Prelude: Group Activities.
One member of the group
lies on his side.
Another person lies down
facing the back of the first
and puts his arms around
his partner's stomach.
The next person takes the same
position behind the second
and so on.
When the entire group is together
in this manner,
take time to experience.
The last person in line gets up
and comes to the front of the
line. Continue
until the original person is at
the end of the line.
Feel the group.
The group may try to rise
all together.

Being

Hands in a Dome

Prelude: Group Activities.
The group joins together
in a circle.
Close your eyes. Each person
places one hand in the center
of the circle, one on top
of the other, then the other
hand. Feel all the hands
in the center of
the circle.
Slowly, simultaneously
raise all the hands to shoulder
level. Hold them there
for a few seconds.
Slowly lower your hands
to waist level.
This time raise all
hands overhead
(still holding on).
Slowly lower to waist level.
The final time, raise your arms
as far as they will go
over your heads.
Slowly allow your arms to lower
to your sides.
Experience how you feel.
Open your eyes.
See one another.

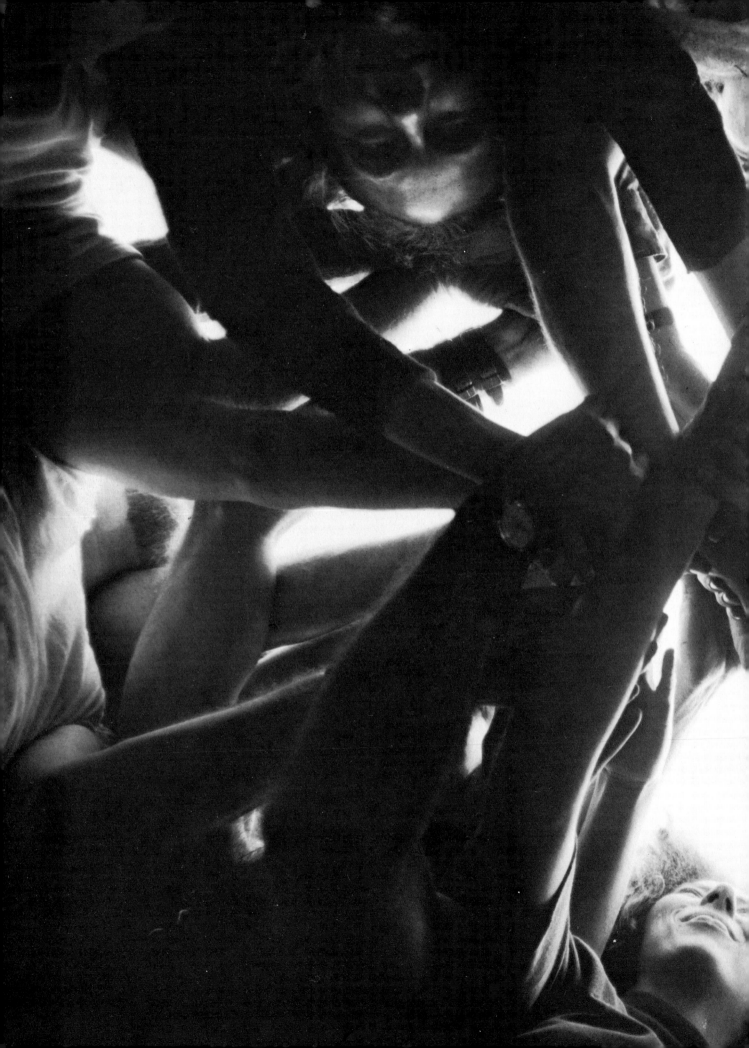